THE CRIMSON THRONE

Praise for *The Ascetic of Desire*

'A lushly sensual and thoughtful debut novel . . . Kakar offers a tantalizing view of how sex is constructed, dreamed, subdued and performed in culturally specific contexts and through history, rich folklore and marvellous parables'—*Publishers Weekly*

'Fascinating reading . . . Sudhir Kakar has reconstructed [Vatsyayana's] life and times with the consummate skill of a master-craftsman'—Khushwant Singh in *The Tribune*

'A journey into the furthest past, an ecstatic dream beyond all time'—*Vogue*, Germany

Praise for *Ecstasy*

'This novel dramatizes, as only good fiction can, that even in reading about transgendered breasts and transcendent visions we are, finally, reading about aspects of ourselves'—*Washington Post Book World*

'What holds the narrative together is Kakar's sympathetic descriptions of religious life—the set piece in a temple that specializes in exorcism is a classic. His prose is clear and evocative'—*The Hindu*

'Kakar excels in turning his cultural and spiritual heritage into a narrative of identity'
—*India Today*

'A mesmeric and readable book about a mysticism which tantalises as it recedes in a haze and dust of contemporary revivalism'—*Deccan Chronicle*

'Eminently readable . . . deserves the attention of all serious-minded people'
—Khushwant Singh in *The Telegraph*

'With sensitivity and intelligence, Kakar's *Ecstasy* offers a poetic view of the place where flesh and spirit meet'—*The Seattle Times*

Praise for *Mira and the Mahatma*

'Skillful manipulation of time enables Sudhir Kakar to reclaim a space between history and imagination . . . a beautifully written novel'—*The Telegraph*

'*Mira and the Mahatma* is [Kakar's] best book. It makes one fall in love with Bapu'
—Khushwant Singh in *The Tribune*

'Not only brilliantly researched but also grippingly narrated. With his third novel, [Kakar] has established a unique niche for himself in the world of Indian English fiction'—*India Today*

'A love story, made all the more poignant by the agony it caused both . . . Kakar's Gandhi is supremely relevant for today'—Mark Tully in *Outlook*

'A sublime, sensual portrait of the Mahatma'—*Hindustan Times*

'Kakar weaves a vivid portrait of those extraordinary years in India's history . . . a must for all those fascinated by the freedom movement and its moral underpinnings'
—*Business Standard*

'Perhaps the most passionate of platonic love relationships of all times'
—*Neue Zuricher Zeitung*, Zurich

The Crimson Throne

SUDHIR KAKAR

PENGUIN
VIKING

VIKING

Published by the Penguin Group

Penguin Books India Pvt. Ltd, 11 Community Centre, Panchsheel Park,
New Delhi 110 017, India

Penguin Group (USA) Inc., 375 Hudson Street, New York, New York 10014, USA

Penguin Group (Canada), 90 Eglinton Avenue East, Suite 700, Toronto, Ontario,
M4P 2Y3, Canada (a division of Pearson Penguin Canada Inc.)

Penguin Books Ltd, 80 Strand, London WC2R 0RL, England

Penguin Ireland, 25 St Stephen's Green, Dublin 2, Ireland (a division of Penguin Books
Ltd)

Penguin Group (Australia), 250 Camberwell Road, Camberwell, Victoria 3124,
Australia (a division of Pearson Australia Group Pty Ltd)

Penguin Group (NZ), 67 Apollo Drive One, Rosedale, North Shore 0632,
New Zealand (a division of Pearson New Zealand Ltd)

Penguin Group (South Africa) (Pty) Ltd, 24 Sturdee Avenue, Rosebank,
Johannesburg 2196, South Africa

Penguin Books Ltd, Registered Offices: 80 Strand, London WC2R 0RL, England

First published in Viking by Penguin Books India 2010

Copyright © Sudhir Kakar 2010

ISBN 9780670084104

For sale in the Indian Subcontinent only

Typeset in Californian FB by R. Ajith Kumar, New Delhi
Printed at Chaman Offset Printers, Delhi

To the memory of my dear friends
Ali Baquer and Vijay Pillai

'The story of any momentous event in history is told and re-told in different eras by many different voices, in varied contexts and for many different audiences.'

—From *The Linguistics of History*, Roy Harris

'History is the present. That's why every generation writes it anew. But what most people think of as history is its end product, myth.'

—E.L. Doctorow

Prologue

MY FRIEND KHWAJA CHISTI is an optimist. He does not think we are witnessing the beginning of the end of the greatest empire on earth. But then, he is not completely of our tribe. Something went awry when he was being castrated. He still feels remnants of the urgings that compel men to ignore what is plainly in sight, or to espy what is not there. Eunuchs, by nature, are realists. Our eyes have long stopped being seduced by illusion.

We are sitting in my quarters in the royal harem on an early August afternoon. The usual sounds of the harem, which normally resemble the high-pitched chatter of an aviary at the break of dawn, have reduced to the distant mumble of a mountain stream. Latticed blinds have been lowered to cover the entrances to the apartments of the queens and princesses to shut out the glare of the sun. Almost all the maids and slave girls have retired to their chowk adjoining the walls of the fort. Matrons entrusted with the task of looking after the harem squat in groups of three or four on the veined marble floors of the broad verandas outside the apartments, gossiping in voices that barely rise above a whisper. A few of them have dozed off, their legs stretched out in front of them as they lean against the cool marble pillars. The emperor, too, has retired for his afternoon siesta, and I am free for a couple of hours till he awakens and prepares to attend court at five in the evening.

Chisti and I are old friends who share the special bond of being emasculated on the same day. I was nine, Chisti a year younger. We have done well for ourselves. Chisti is the chief eunuch in the harem of Danishmand Khan, the emperor's advisor on foreign affairs. I serve the emperor himself and hope to soon be raised to the rank of a senior eunuch. I will enjoy being a Nazir.

'Khwaja!' I tell him, 'Empires are like human beings that begin to die the moment they are born. The emperor Akbar was the high noon of the Mughul empire and our own sovereign is its setting sun. Praise Allah that we have lived in the time of the empire's greatest splendour. If it was also the time of its greatest decadence, then that is the nature of all empires. After us no more Taj Mahals shall be built. Delhi will never again be the magnet that attracts the best jewellers in the world to craft another Peacock Throne. The treasury of the emperor of Hindustan will never again bulge with such vast quantities of gold, silver and precious stones as it does today. The Mughal armies will never again be so victorious as they were during the thirty years of Shah Jahan's reign.'

'If you are such a great historian, Niamat,' Chisti says, his eyes narrowing with characteristic scorn, 'then tell me why the House of Timur is fated to disappear.'

'I am not a historian,' I say, ignoring his sarcasm, 'but I am one of the emperor's personal attendants. I can pick up the whiff of decay emanating from the centre of the empire that has not yet reached other nostrils. You only see the brilliant light of today's fire; I see tomorrow's ashes. If you want to call me anything then call me a visionary. Historians look at the past, I look into the future. They are concerned with beginnings, I envision ends. But if you insist on asking "why", then I will say that the will to govern, to rule, is lost, my friend. I look around at the dazzling splendour of the court, and all I see is an emptiness of purpose. Our emperor is tired and seeks rejuvenation in women's bodies. The Wali Ahad values learning more than governance. The only prince whose will to rule is intact is a bigot. He has the pride, hardness and cunning an emperor needs, but does he also possess the wisdom to make these qualities means to achieve great ends?'

I can see Chisti's eyes begin to get a glassy look. I am aware that he thinks I monopolize our conversations, that I am often too serious, even portentous. I pass him the hukka and ask him about the latest court gossip. Chisti becomes animated. He is in his element now. The hukka gurgles happily. Intrigues are rampant, conspiracies abound. The nobles are dividing into factions that form and reform like remnants of monsoon clouds racing aimlessly into each other across the August sky. He lowers his voice when he comes to the escapades of the royal princesses. We chuckle over their sexual appetites that match those of the men of the House of Timur. My attention begins to wander once his stories become uneventful. Two *farangi* doctors have recently joined the court . . .

Khwaja Chisti is my oldest friend but I wish he were less longwinded.

*'Even when there is darkness all around, a star
lights my path alone'*

NICCOLAO MANUCCI

I BELIEVE I HAVE been singularly favoured by fortune ever since my birth in 1631, the year that the plague, which decimated almost a quarter of Venice's population, finally retreated. That my impoverished parents survived the plague in one of the most wretched parts of the city, overrun by garbage and rats, when it did not spare even the Doge and his family, can only be a miracle.

'My little Niccolao,' my mother would say, 'your birth was a sign from God that after a decade of death Venice was once again ripe for new life.'

For the most part of my life, even in the most adverse circumstances, I have known that I am being watched over by a benign Providence. Even when there is darkness all around, a star lights my path alone. How else could it be that I, who grew up on the docks of Venice, and found my way to distant Hindustan where I was welcomed into the mansions of the nobility, received at the court of the Great Mogul himself, became a confidant to the Crown Prince, or the Wali Ahad as

4

his subjects addressed him, took part in the war of succession to the throne of the Mogul empire and, above all, became rich and famous for my proficiency in the healing arts? Especially since I had not studied medicine in Italy. Or, for that matter, studied anything at all, anywhere.

Not that I am ashamed of my low birth, or my lack of a formal education. I have acquired my education in the school of life and I owe my success to the lessons it has taught me. Neither have I neglected to use my God-given gifts. A gift for learning languages, for instance. Within a year of my arrival in Hindustan, in the Portuguese stronghold of Goa, I could speak fluent Persian and Portuguese and a fair smattering of the native tongue of the Hindus. I also have a talent for passionate speech and find it easy for me to bring people around to my views. I can usually convince them to follow a course of action that they might be hesitant about but which I hold to be correct. In the years of my youth, of which I write, I was often told that my grey eyes, bronzed curls and manly chin with the hint of a cleft aided my persuasive ways.

But what good would these gifts have been without the opportunity to use them to any effect? India gave me this opportunity, as it still does to poor but adventurous European youth.

The day my ship docked at the port of Goa on the last Sunday of March 1653, after a seventy-day voyage around the Cape of Good Hope, the captain, a middle-aged Neapolitan on his last voyage to the Indies, called me to his cabin as I was preparing to go ashore. At sea, he had been a strict taskmaster. My swabbing of the decks, a task I performed to pay for my passage to India, had never managed to meet his high standards. Now, with the ship safely anchored, his normally stern expression had seeped away, like water into sand. He was reclining on his bunk bed, his boots thrown carelessly on the floor, a near-empty bottle of rum precariously wedged between his slack thighs. The cabin reeked of sweaty feet, dirty socks and alcohol fumes.

'Look for shelter with one of the Christian orders, Niccolao,' he said as he handed me a few ducats he had pulled out of the pocket of his dirty coat. 'These church vermin live shamelessly off the land and the sweat of its people, but some of them are too afraid of the Lord not to have an occasional kind impulse. They're your best bet, boy.'

My first steps on the wharf were an unsteady pirouette. I was as one intoxicated, as much from the portents of a glorious future as from the beauty of the surroundings, which my eyes had imbibed since the previous afternoon. As I scrubbed the deck for the last time, I watched the waves ripple through the pale aquamarine sea and gently lap the beaches of fine white sand. The next morning, a warm breeze bearing the premonition of a hot day gently blew over the ship as it entered the mouth of the river Mandovi from the sea where it had been for the night. The mist that had hovered above ground and stretched almost halfway towards the chain of blue hills in the distance had begun to lift. As the ship sailed towards the port of Goa, some ten kilometres inland, I marvelled at the lush, impenetrable, dark green mangroves intersected by narrow creeks that exuded a faintly menacing air. Thatched huts had peered out of thick coconut groves. Further inland, closer to our destination, the dwellings on the riverbank were transformed. Grand villas with sprawling gardens of exotic plants came into view, their strange flowers bursting in vivid colour. My spirit soared. I could already see myself as the owner of one of these mansions. In Venice, I had often walked past the palaces of the nobility—the Barbaros, Pisianis, Grimanis, Padavins, Ottobans—gaping at their grand palazzos in envy, tinged always with longing. I would never have been allowed to enter those palaces, even as a servant; they were as inaccessible to me as would be the seraglios of the emperors of China or India.

My mother had died when I was seven years old. My father, the least happy man I ever knew, worked on the docks loading and unloading ships. He had neither the means nor the inclination to look after a growing boy. I was largely left to fend for myself. Sleep to me meant a dirty mattress spread on a stone floor. Food was an occasional stew of sardines and potatoes growing cold on a grease-spattered, unlit iron stove. Home was infrequent glimpses of a father who returned late at night, drunk, and felt no compunction in beating me awake, for past transgressions neither of us remembered, or in advance for sins I was yet to commit. I had grown up on my own on the streets and docks of Venice, honing my wits, listening to the fantastical tales sailors spun of their travels in distant lands, and nurturing my fevered dreams of escape to the legendary lands of the East.

'The houses of the Portuguese in Goa do not have a scrap of iron,' I would hear the sailors say. 'Everything in them is made either of gold or silver.' The Portuguese, I was told, thought so little of gold that they used it liberally to paint and adorn the beams, doorways and window frames of their houses. Their beds were made of fragrant aloe wood and had gold feet. The sprawling rooms in the mansions where rich merchants lived were swept with brooms with handles made of gold. When the lady of the house stepped out, two women servants walked alongside her litter with gold incensers and gently blew the fragrant smoke into the litter with Japanese ivory fans to protect her from the stench and miasma of sickness and disease on the street.

'From Goa,' the sailors said, 'young men less than your age make but two or three voyages to Japan or China, Malacca or the Philippines. On their return, they sell goods they bring back with them at five or six times the cost. Soon, they acquire riches beyond imagination.' Even discounting the exaggeration arising from a liberal partaking of our fine Italian wine after months spent at sea, the sailors' stories of Goa's fabled riches were heady enough for a youth with ambition but no prospects.

Now, having arrived in the land of my dreams, I could see myself as lord and master of a tropical villa in Goa, being waited on by a host of native servants, sharing my bed with dusky Indian maidens with lissome limbs. Satiated and wealthy, I would return to Venice after a few years with a head full of stories and wooden chests crammed with silver and gold. Ah, youth! When the future is a sky ablaze with light and life but a parade of dreams!

The disenchantment came later, when I was no longer standing on the deck of a ship gliding on water but walking on earth. It began as I wandered Goa's cobbled streets and saw the city of my dreams start to crumble before my eyes with each step I took.

Built from a porous, laterite stone the colour of dried blood, found in abundance in these parts, Goa had more than a hundred palaces that must have been splendid at one time. In more than a hundred years of Portuguese presence, the city flourished as the capital of Portuguese possessions in the East. It was a centre of commerce and Christian faith. But by the time I arrived, Goa had slid far down along the slope of decline. Save for the main cathedrals, seminaries and convents of the larger religious orders, most buildings were shabby and ill-kept. The once splendid mansions were on their way to becoming equally spectacular ruins. Scorched yellow palms drooped in gardens that had not been tended to in years and were now overwhelmed by weeds. Window panes, made not from glass but from thin polished oyster shells set in wooden frames, were grimy with dust and speckled with lozenge-shaped holes where broken shells had not been replaced. There were few carriages on the streets. Most people walked. I discovered, too late, that the wondrous Goa of the tales I had heard in the taverns of Venice, the Goa of gold and silver for which I had sailed so far, had ceased to exist around the time I was born.

There was the competition, of course. Other Europeans, especially the Dutch, who had deprived the Portuguese of their trade by interdicting their sea routes and gaining control of the route to the Moluccas and the Spice Islands. The English, too, reigned supreme in the Persian Gulf after their capture of Ormuz. With the loss of their monopoly over trade in the East, gold and silver no longer flowed into Goa as had happened for most of the last century.

The more I explored the city, my steps no longer spritely, my spirit weighed down by the ruin, decay and lawlessness I saw around me, the more convinced I became that the haughty Portuguese had brought this fate upon themselves. Their ancestors had been distinguished by courage, a zeal for religion and grand exploits. Indian princes, without exception, had courted their friendship. But the present generation of the Portuguese in India seemed to revel in being petty, mean and unnecessarily cruel, addicted to every imaginable vice and shallow pleasure.

What happens to the Portuguese, to these simple Iberian lads, when they first come out to the East, I wonder. No sooner has their ship rounded the Cape of Good Hope than they become *fidalgos*, gentlemen. Each one of them adds a 'Don' to the simple Pedro or Mario by which he was known just a fraction of time earlier. And as their names change, their natures too undergo—an alarming transformation. They become violent, mean-spirited and treat others—especially the native Hindus—with utter disdain. I found the Hindus, most of whom had by then retreated inland to remote villages, to be utterly cowed down. If some of them had to come to the city on business, they could be seen scurrying along the main street with their heads bowed and shoulders hunched. They may not be conversant with the true faith, and their own religion may be incomprehensible to outsiders, yet they too are human, even if sorely misguided, and deserve Christian compassion.

The Portuguese also despised the native Christians, who were either converted Hindus or the much more numerous *mestica*, the mixed breed of Portuguese and Indian blood. But unlike the meeker Hindus, the *mestica* returned the compliment by openly calling the Portuguese arrogant and ill-mannered. I found the *mestica* men to be generally amiable and easy-going. Having spent many agreeable evenings in their taverns I can say of them that they are honest drinkers who drink for the purpose and to the point of intoxication. They also love to sing. My first lessons in Portuguese were acquired by the unusual method of joining them in their drunken singing, which went from bawdy to melancholy as the evening progressed. In return, I taught them Italian curse words I had picked up on the docks of Venice. Soon, they were using *iglio di puttana*, son of a whore, and *cornuto*, cuckold, as terms of endearment for each other. 'Your language is so musical,' they said.

Even among themselves, the Portuguese are a vindictive lot. I have seen no other nation whose men are as jealous of their women as the Portuguese of Goa. If a *fidalgo* entertains the least suspicion about his woman he will not hesitate to do away with her by poison or dagger. The man involved in the affair rarely escapes death. He is sought out and killed by the cuckold's Kaffirs, black slaves imported from Mozambique, wherever they find him, even in a sacred place. As I prayed in church one Sunday morning, about a month after my arrival, I witnessed the most gruesome of crimes. Three slaves came running up the aisle, and a man who had been kneeling two rows ahead of me made a dash towards the altar. Unmindful of where they were and of the screams of the parishioners the Kaffirs discharged their blunderbusses at his retreating back. Two innocent bystanders were killed and the priest was wounded in the shoulder. The man himself escaped and fled Goa the same day.

I too had a narrow escape once. One of these *fidalgo*s, with his ridiculous sense of honour, felt he needed to avenge himself under the false impression that I was putting the horns on him. I shall tell that story in its proper place. Here, I only wish to say that I did not leave Goa because of that incident. That is a despicable lie, a malicious rumour spread by my enemies at the Mogul court. I shall not be surprised at that lying Frenchman M. Bernier's involvement in its dissemination. It was simply time for me to leave Goa to seek my fortune further north, in the heart of the Mogul empire.

The anarchy prevailing in Goa was, in fact, worse than what one encounters in the most violent quarters of any European port. I learned from my *mestica* friends that till a few months before my arrival bands of Kaffirs freely roamed the city at night, intent on robbery and murder. At one time, when Goa was prospering, rich merchants would employ fifty or even a hundred African slaves, but as times changed they let the slaves go. Feared and despised, and with no means of earning an honest living, the Kaffirs took to waylaying and killing anyone foolish enough to be out at night and plundering lightly guarded houses. Finally, they became bold enough to attack Portuguese soldiers. Each day a dozen or more guards would be found lying dead in the streets, with the result that the Viceroy ordered a curfew on the Kaffirs from eight at night till six in the morning. Night patrols were increased and the soldiers instructed to kill any Kaffirs they encountered wandering the streets after the curfew hour. On the very first morning after the Viceroy's order, two hundred corpses of the poor wretches were found in various parts of the city. This continued for a week till the Kaffirs were intimidated. Not that the Portuguese guards were much better than the Kaffirs. Robberies and murders may have decreased, but assaults and rapes became more common.

Though threatened, the Kaffirs did not disappear from the streets but simply broke into smaller bands. They now did their robbing in the afternoon and at smoky dusk before the night curfew began. Hindu shopkeepers in the outskirts of the city, who could not afford to employ guards, faced the worst of it. They kept the doors of their shops locked from inside even during the day and made large holes in the door through which they received money and handed out articles of daily use. But even this precaution was not enough. Apparently, six months before my arrival, two Kaffirs approached a shopkeeper, pretending to buy twenty red peppers. When the shopkeeper extended his hand for the money, one of the Kaffirs seized it and held it down while the other pricked it continuously with a knife, threatening to cut off the hand if the shopkeeper did not give them all of his money. The petrified shopkeeper called out to his wife to gather all the money in the house and give it to them. But the Kaffirs still cut off two of the man's fingers before releasing his hand. He had given them two chillies less, they said. Following this incident, Hindu shopkeepers no longer extended their hands through the hole. Instead, they used long wooden spoons to supply goods and accept money in exchange.

You may ask why I spent a year in Goa if my prospects of making a quick fortune through voyages to China and Japan had disappeared even before I arrived. In reply, I can only point to my guiding star.

Here, too, it played its part. As I stepped on to the wharf, remembering the captain's advice, I requested a passerby to direct me to the living quarters of a Christian order nearby. He pointed to the top of a hill in the distance where a large whitewashed house with handsome galleries stood like a bastion. Imagine my surprise when I found it was a convent run by Italian monks of the Franciscan order. The prior turned out to be a Neapolitan who welcomed me with genuine affection. He told me that I could stay with them for as long as I liked.

The convent of the Franciscans became my home for the next twelve months. Nothing could have been more fortuitous, and I say this for two reasons. First, the elevated position of the house assured a constant flow of fresh breeze that kept the pestilence of the town at bay. In all of my stay in Goa, I was not sick for even a single day. Second, a missionary doctor, Father Luigi Rossi, or Luigi as I like to think of him, took me under his wing and instructed me in the medical arts. He gave me a profession that changed my life, though not my dream.

'My intention is to be a witness, no more than ears and eyes to remarkable happenings'

FRANCOIS BERNIER

WHEN I FIRST SET out for India twenty-five years ago, my intention had been to provide my anonymous readers and well-known patrons in France with an accurate account of a land, of its wealth and wonders, that have continued to fascinate the European imagination since the time of Herodotus. I could hardly imagine then that I would also become the sole European to record the facts and occurrences in the upheavals that beset the empire of the Great Mogul, Emperor Shah Jahan.

From the zeal I have for the service of our great sovereign Louis XIV and the honour of France, I have thought it my duty to render an account of my observations on what I have seen in my travels to the Mogul empire of the Indies and thus to pour out into the bosom of France what I have amassed in India. My object in this work is not merely to assuage public curiosity. I propose for myself a more noble and elevated aim: to reveal to my countrymen through a comparison with the famed empire of the Indies how fortunate we are to live in

France. I venture to say I have done so with more boldness and even greater success than those travellers who have been more fortunate in being born with a title or to wealth.

My hope is that this account of my travels will meet the expectations of learned and discerning personages. If they find these memoirs written in a style devoid of elegance then I hope they will not consider it extraordinary that during the long absence of twelve years from France my language may have become semi-barbarous. If I have interposed in certain places stories which might relieve the mind after descriptions of land, people and travel, I have done so in imitation of the orientals who establish caravanserais at intervals in their deserts to provide relief to travellers. My purpose throughout this account, however, is instruction and elevation rather than amusement and diversion. I acknowledge that because of my interest in politics and the social life of a land, I have neglected the reader who is connected with commerce and desires to know what India produces, through art and nature, for the enjoyment of European nations.

I do not hesitate to admit that given my sober, even earnest, disposition I am not the ideal person to introduce a foreign land and its people. The Indians maintain that the mind of a man cannot always be occupied with serious affairs, and that he remains forever a child in this respect. To develop what is good in him, almost as much care must be taken to amuse him as cause him to study. The Indians—and I speak not of the believers in the religion of Mohammed but of the Gentile idolaters—for all their claims to antiquity, are a surprisingly young, even childishly naïve race in their approach to serious affairs, of state or, indeed, of life. Yet there is merit to their argument, since some of our more pessimistic European philosophers, despairing of the human capacity for seriousness, have grudgingly conceded that the more abstract the matter you wish to teach, the more you will have to seduce the senses to it.

Although I agree with Plutarch that trifling incidents—whose main source in the Indies is bazaar gossip—ought not to be concealed as they often enable us to form more accurate opinions of the genius of a people and their monarchs than events of signal importance, I prefer to be a sober observer of people and events in order that my record of them will one day be deemed accurate history. Thus, unlike most Indians, who tend towards frivolity—and a certain Italian quack who dispenses potions to the credulous at the imperial court and dignifies all manner of gossip—I view people's appearance or apparel, their manners and customs, learning and pursuits, beliefs and habits, mores and morals as more instructive than diverting and thus more attuned to the taste of my intended audience that is as educated as it is discriminating. This does not mean that I will excise my account of every trifling incident; I hold only that any such incident included in a serious history be truthful and not have its birth in the fancy of the populace, or that of the writer.

Before beginning my account, I shall briefly introduce myself, not in the manner of a braggart hoping for applause for achievements that loom large in his own mind alone, but to acquaint the reader with my origins and possible prejudices so that he may better judge the accuracy of my opinions and, if he finds it advisable, discount some of my conclusions.

I was born on the twenty-fifth day of September, 1620, at Joue, near Gonnard, in Anjou. My parents were honest and devout; my father was a yeoman who leased and cultivated land that belonged to the Canonery of St Maurice at Angers in the Barony of Etiau. My aquiline features and high-domed forehead bear no trace of my peasant ancestry, I have often been told, an intended compliment that gratifies me less at present than it did when I was younger.

The only vivid memory I have of my early years is of looking up at my father's powerful shoulders bunched between the shafts of a horse-plough, his narrowed eyes fixed on the ground, his clicking tongue goading the horses forward, while I stumbled around the farm in his broad shadow. I became an orphan at the age of five when my parents were taken by a mysterious fever, and was cared for by my uncle, the curé de Chanzaux, till the age of fifteen, when I moved to Paris to study at the Collège de Clermont.

Since my intention in these memoirs is to be a witness, no more than ears and eyes to remarkable happenings, I shall keep an account of how a peasant's son came to travel in the lands of Eastern potentates to a minimum. Suffice to say that when I was entering my youth, a series of fortunate events brought me to the attention of M. Pierre Gassendi, the famous philosopher. M. Gassendi adopted me as his protégé and took personal charge of my education. Indeed, that great man whom many consider as the heir of Montaigne, did me the signal honour of employing me as his secretary before he died. He also graciously invited me to move into his own house, where I was to occupy a spacious, well-lit room with a large bay window with a pleasing prospect of the garden. His beneficence allowed me to give up my ill-furnished room in a boarding house on Rue Pierre-a-Poisson where each morning I had to make my way past shouting fishmongers and their jostling customers, sometimes being pushed against long tables heaped with river fish and at other times avoiding rats scurrying through the stinking fish offal.

The character of M. Gassendi's intellect, both inventive and critical, the liveliness of his imagination and the retentiveness of his memory, have been earlier commented on by his many admirers and colleagues, who are infinitely more erudite and better judges of his contributions to the world of knowledge than I can ever hope to be. What these personages have not sufficiently stressed is his curiosity about distant lands, a curiosity he passed on to me as his inheritance. My travels were, thus, not undertaken as a result of the feelings of unsettledness that routinely beset young men, but were driven by a thirst to know and compare rather than merely see and enjoy the towns and countryside, the inhabitants and productions, of a foreign land.

It was on M. Gassendi's advice that I studied medicine before setting out on my travels. While preparing me for the examination in physiology at the University of Montpellier, he often reiterated his conviction that of all professions a doctor was the most reliable guide to the understanding of foreign peoples and their mores. 'You will know more about other people by helping them than by merely observing them. If you would gain knowledge of a man, it is better to do things *for* him and *with* him than to stand apart or, worse, do things *to* him,' he said. M. Gassendi's wisdom was not a whit less than the generosity of his spirit.

After graduating as licentiate in medicine in 1652, I spent most of my nights as a young resident surgeon among the Gothic portals of Hospital Dieu, its long passages crammed with sick-beds, reading Father Monserrate's account of his years at the court of Akbar, the grandfather of the present emperor Shah Jahan; all three volumes of Father Pierre du Jarric's *Histoire de Choses plus Memorables Advenues*; and two volumes of the Italian Pietro della Valle's travels in India.

'Study these books well, Bernier,' M. Gassendi would say, 'and you may reasonably hope to arrive in India a stranger, yet one who will not be shocked by that weird and wonderful country's onslaught on a visitor's senses and reason.'

Like most accounts of travel, these volumes were often tedious reading for me. I freely concede that my interests are not all-encompassing. I am often as one blind to the physical features of a land: to its flora and fauna, to the habitat and habitations of its people. My curiosity, influenced no doubt by the example of my esteemed teacher, prefers to dwell on human beings and, if afforded an opportunity, dart into their characters.

Once in India, I had hoped to go to the Mogul court in Delhi as soon as possible to offer my services as a physician. European physicians, I had heard, were considered superior to native Mohammedan hakims and the idolater vaids in most branches of medicine, particularly in the treatment of war wounds. While a resident at Hospital Dieu in France I had worked under the guidance of M. Pissier, himself a pupil of the renowned surgeon Ambrois Parre, who had revolutionized the care of amputated stumps on the battlefield. (War is indeed the mother of all invention!) I was well versed in the care of such injuries and in employing the Parre method of tying off arteries to control bleeding, followed by the application of an ointment prepared from a cold mix of egg yolk, rose oil and turpentine to the wound, thus eliminating the old method of cauterizing the bleeding part with a red-hot iron or boiling oil. I was aware that native doctors were unfamiliar with such medical advancements and was thus sanguine about my prospects of finding honourable employment at the Mogul court. I could have never foreseen at the time that at the end of my eleven-year stay in the country, I would be holding the position of a personal physician to the emperor himself!

It was well into the spring of 1657 when I finally boarded a vessel which brought me to Surat, a bustling port on the west coast of India on the bank of a river nine leagues inland from the sea. My funds were nowhere near exhaustion, but possessing the prudence of age while still a youth I did not wish to tarry in Surat for even a day more than necessary. I had made up my mind to proceed immediately to the imperial court in Delhi. Providence, however, decreed that I postpone my departure for almost three weeks while I recovered from a mysterious tropical ailment. This unforeseen delay was a godsend as it enabled me to become more familiar with the country, by now absorbing it through the senses rather than through books.

If my memories of Surat are blurred then it is not only due to the fastidious nature of my cognition but also, and more prosaically, because I was indisposed with a low fever and loss of appetite for most of these days. I was fortunate to find shelter at the residence of M. Briffault, a fine and noble gentleman who liked to dress in loose Indian robes, wore a monocle in the English fashion and who had been deputed by our monarch to explore the possibility of establishing a French factory in Surat. I therefore spent the most vulnerable days of my travels—when I was physically ill in a country which can be forbidding to a European encountering it for the first time—in an ambience which, if not totally French, was also not quite Indian, thus providing me with a transitional haven when I needed one the most.

My first impressions of India were mainly gathered from the windows of M. Briffault's carriage, which my host, who sometimes accompanied me on these outings, graciously put at my disposal after the bout of fever had passed and I had begun to regain my strength.

What struck me the most was the sheer number and variety of people on the streets, more than I would ever see in Paris or Marseilles. Their complexions ranged from Persian pale to Negro teak and they were garbed in diverse dress and headgear. This diversity, however, was not raw confusion but presented a pattern to the initiated eye. 'You will notice, M. Bernier,' M. Briffault had said, 'that the turbans the Mohammedans wear are white and round while those of the idolaters are coloured, straight, high and pointed. And if you're wondering at the crowds in the streets and in the bazaars, you will need to return here in the monsoon when the country is lashed by heavy rains. During those months ships avoid the open seas and seek shelter here. They are loaded with merchandise as they wait and the town is so full of people that it is almost impossible to find lodging.'

Although the idolater men are generally short and unprepossessing, their darkly bronzed women with bold black eyes and glossy black hair, tied in a bun behind the neck or twisted in the form of a pyramid above the head, hold an undeniable attraction which, some might say, is less aesthetic than basely visceral. I am speaking, of course, only of the idolater women of lower classes who walk on the street with their faces uncovered. The upper-class women, both idolater and Mohammedan, are carried in decorated palanquins closed on all sides, with a thick piece of silk curtaining the two tiny windows and the entrance. Even the poorer Mohammedan women on the country, like the women of Turkey and Persia, never venture out on the street unveiled. They cover themselves with a white shroud that falls down to their ankles and has a narrow slit covered with a fine net in front of the eyes. The dress of the idolater women is generally a simple cotton cloth, white or coloured, which is bound five or six times like a petticoat from the waist downwards, with cunning folds in front that makes it look as if they are wearing three or four petticoats, one above the other. Well-born women throw one end of this cloth across their breasts while those belonging to the lower tribes are indifferent about the matter. Indeed, the Banjara women, a nomad folk who transport goods from one part of the country to another and are thus often encountered in groups on the streets of Surat, tattoo their skin from the waist upwards with flowers, which are then painted in different colours with the juice of roots. I was always quick to avert my gaze from Banjara girls although I can well imagine that the sight of their firm breasts and sooty, prominent nipples, colourfully decorated in this manner, can be occasion for concupiscent excitement in men with a lewd disposition.

I found M. Briffault a congenial companion who shared my liberal persuasion, which proved often to be at odds with that of the other Europeans with whom I made acquaintance. These were no more than twenty in number and were all attached to the English and Dutch factories in Surat. The worst of these was a Mr Charles Morley who ran the English factory and who, M. Briffault informed me, was overly fond of catamites in which the Indies abounds. A stout man, whose ill-fitting wig accentuated his balding pate rather than hiding it, Mr Morley had lived in India for eleven years and regarded himself as an authority on the land and its peoples. For some inexplicable reason, this man took a liking to me in a rare contradiction of M. Gassendi's adage 'If you do not like a person, Bernier, you can be certain that the person also dislikes you', and sought every opportunity to turn up at M. Briffault's house in the evening to enlighten me on the imperfections of this country and the utter stupidity of the idolaters who constitute by far the largest part of its population.

'Do you know, M. Bernier, that they run hospices for cows, horses, dogs, cats and even insects and flies? Is that not a testimony to the boundless foolishness of these people? In one of these hospices, I saw a white-bearded venerable old man diligently feeding little orphaned mice milk with a bird's feather because they were so small that they could eat nothing else!'

'M. Bernier, do not believe all that Morley says about the idolaters. His facts may be right but his judgements are seriously flawed,' M. Briffault said after the Englishman had left. 'The idolaters of Surat are indeed an odd people who do not eat meat of any kind, preferring to subsist on tasteless vegetables and lentil gruel. They are, however, no more eccentric than the rest of their race whose religious beliefs and living habits would appear ludicrous to any right-thinking Christian. Personally, I find the idolaters of India a race that is more unfortunate than depraved. Belonging to an earlier stage of mental if not material development—for they are capable of manufacturing the most exquisite goods—the idolaters can hold up to us a mirror of a past which we left behind when our Christian faith delivered us from the superstition and idolatry that still holds the people of the Indies in an iron thrall.

'Not that the kind of Europeans found in Surat are much better,' he continued. 'They are but the riff-raff of our continent who drift into the Indies and, God knows, do not do Europe proud. Many of them try to smuggle goods past the customs when they land in Surat, especially gold, for which the idolaters have an insatiable appetite and which they hoard with an avarice that beggars imagination. The English are the worst. When they adopted from Europe the fashion of wearing wigs, they came up with the ingenious notion of concealing Jacobuses, rose-nobles and ducats in the nets of their wigs every time they left their vessels to go ashore. Emperor Shah Jahan looks indulgently on attempts at smuggling, viewing it as a game of ingenuity between the smugglers and his officials. Anyone caught smuggling merely pays ten instead of the normal five per cent duty on the goods. Because of the kind of European who makes his way into India, the whole continent has got a bad reputation among upper-class Indians as home to a dishonest people lacking finer sensibilities and impelled solely by greed and avarice.'

As my strength returned, my carriage rides became more frequent. In the evening, before the sun had set and a cool breeze began to come up the river from the sea, I would alight on the quay to take in the air on the bank of the river that was crowded with ships and innumerable small boats racing up and down on the sweet water. Ships from far-off regions of the world—Europe, Persia, Arabia, Basra, Siam, Acheen, Malacca, Batavia, Manila, China—as also from Malabar and Bengal in the Indies, seemed to be regular arrivals at the country's busiest port.

Yet, for all its fabled wealth, I found Surat lagging behind Marseilles in the magnificence of its public buildings. Whereas Marseilles is a fortified port enclosed by Italianate quays and is overlooked by the town and two newly constructed forts, Surat was but a sprawl on both banks of the river with just a small fortification on one of the banks protecting its commerce. It was a dirty city, with narrow, crooked streets and houses that were no more than huts built of a mix of mud, cow dung and Brushwood broke. The few ornate and splendidly furnished palaces on the river front, hidden among large gardens and thus invisible to the casual visitor, belonged to the governor of Surat and other high officials of the state. Afraid of attracting the covetous gaze of imperial officials, the rich merchants of Surat did not dare to display their wealth. In Marseilles, on the other hand, the mansions of the wealthy with their splendid pale stone façades decorated with raised diamond-shaped tips and sweeping panelled staircases unabashedly line the sloping streets. There was a single occasion when I gathered the courage to venture into a bazaar, but I found it difficult to make my way past the hawkers and the throngs gathered around improvised eateries on pushcarts selling all manner of fried fish and kebabs, with which I was already familiar from my stay in Persia. In my fragile state of health, the pungent smell of spices frying in mustard oil made me retch and I was glad to return to the haven of M. Briffault's charming residence.

One afternoon, as I was dozing in one of the armchairs on the veranda, M. Briffault came bounding up the steps in high excitement.

'M. Bernier, I have news! You have been summoned to the imperial court.' The wide smile on his face was reassurance enough that the directive was a herald of good rather than ill fortune.

'I have just received a message from the governor that Danishmand Khan, who advises the emperor on foreign affairs, commands your presence.'

I must have looked at him with questioning eyes for he continued, 'Such a command is almost always a prelude to an offer of employment. Especially since the governor has been asked to provide you with a well-appointed carriage and two servants to look after your needs on the way. You must hurry and pack. The caravan you will join for your journey to Delhi leaves tomorrow morning.'

There was no possibility of matters remaining secret in that vast land and I could only surmise that the Khan had not only known of my arrival in Surat but had also been aware of my background and accomplishments, however slight they may have been. Danishmand Khan, M. Briffault informed me, was one of the most learned Omrah of the imperial court, intensely curious about other countries, and I had been summoned to his presence because he had heard I was a 'philosopher–healer'. I must acknowledge that I had often spoken of M. Gassendi before M. Briffault's guests, perhaps giving the impression of a greater intellectual intimacy with my mentor than had actually been the case, and had erroneously conveyed that M. Gassendi's learning was also mine. It was thus with trepidation, which came from the sentiment of being somewhat of an impostor, that I began packing my meagre belongings for the thirty-day journey to the court of the Great Mogul.

'The first teacher of my body and the
two teachers of my mind'

NICCOLAO MANUCCI

TO THIS DAY I do not know why Luigi chose me as his friend—as much as permitted by the disparity in our ages, of course—since he determinedly avoided other Europeans. I suspected his avoidance was due to an odd physical deformity of which he was acutely self-conscious. Luigi's arms were at least a foot longer than others' and, when he stood, they descended below his knees. With thick red hair that hung low on his forehead and covered the back of his neck, a furry beard that hid most of his face, and a distinctive hunch, he resembled a Barbary ape when he walked.

Luigi was one of those people whose natures totally belie their appearance. Behind his shy smile and a mouthful of crooked yellowing teeth hid the gentlest of hearts. In all the time I knew him, I never heard him speak ill of any man, as if years of ministering to the sick and the poor had erased his ability to make judgements. His voice, strangled in normal conversation, rarely more than a mutter, took wing when he retreated to a corner of the convent's garden in the evening to sing,

24

mainly to himself. The song he sang was always the same: St Francis's haunting hymn:

> *'Dolce sentire come nel mio cuore*
> *Oraumilmente sta nascendo amore.*
> *Dolce capire Che non son' più solo*
> *Ma Che son' parte di una immensa vita*
> *Chegenerosa risplendeintorno a me:*
> *donodi Lui del suo immenso amore.'*

> ('Sweet it is to feel how, in my heart,
> Now, humbly, love is being born.
> Sweet it is to understand, that I am no longer alone,
> But that I am part of an immense life
> That, generously, shines around me,
> Gift of Him, of His immense love.')

Many a time, on my way out to a tavern or my favourite brothel at dusk, when lamps were being lit and the monks were busy with their chores before the dinner bell was rung, I would stand behind the oleander bushes a few yards from the stone bench on which Luigi sat, plucking on his guitar, and listen to the saint's love for God and His creation come pouring out in Luigi's sweet tenor. I could feel the long-buried innocence of my soul seep into my heart as I walked out of the gate, on my way to assuage the cravings of a young man's body. I felt no shame, no guilt. Indeed, it was as though St Francis himself was blessing the urgings of my flesh.

Luigi was wholly given to God's work which, to him, culminated in healing the sick. He would disappear, sometimes for weeks, into the interiors of the country with a horse that carried supplies of drugs and instruments. (In India, the profession of the apothecary is unknown. A doctor must prepare his own medicines and ointments). Whenever he was called upon to treat a sick infant or one on point of death, he would first sprinkle it with the water of baptism. 'In the eight years

I have been here, I must have baptized over fifteen thousand infants,' he told me once we had become friends. 'Now, when I go into their villages, mothers think that sprinkling water on a sick child is part of the treatment.'

Many Hindus, a gentle but excessively superstitious race as I was soon to discover, prostrated themselves on the street when Luigi passed by. One of their most revered gods is the monkey-god, who is also their god of healing. Given his appearance and calling, their obeisance to Luigi was more comprehensible but no less ludicrous. Naturally, to the Inquisition, the whole affair smelt of heresy. I remember how Luigi's voice had quivered as he told me of the time he was summoned before the tribunal. No one takes such summons lightly. It produces fear and trembling even in the most intrepid of men. More than three thousand men and women have spent years in the dungeons under the floor of the hall, where the tribunal meets, merely on grounds of suspicion. Those pronounced guilty of heresy were routinely burnt at the stake in the square in front of the Se Primacial, the Cathedral of St Catherine. Those who confessed their guilt were mercifully strangled before the pyre was lit.

I could imagine Luigi shuffling forward, his accursed arms swinging clumsily before him as he was called before the bench. I could feel the terror he tried to conceal while the tribunal conferred—and the surprise on his face as the Inquisition pronounced its verdict. Luigi's punishment was unique: whenever a Hindu prostrated himself before Luigi, the priest was to mirror the action. No one had ever suspected that the Inquisition had a sense of humour! The nature of Luigi's punishment was one of the compelling reasons that kept him within the four walls of the convent whenever he was in Goa. That his trial was so short was almost certainly due to his lack of worldly goods, of the gold, silver and jewels the Holy Tribunal regularly confiscates to defray its expenses.

In spite of his ordeal, Luigi did not harbour any ill will towards the Inquisition. Years of intercourse with Hindus, especially the Hindu doctor who was also to become my teacher, had infused his already gentle nature with a mildness that I did not appreciate at the time. I even thought of it as unmanly.

I had not received any formal education in my youth but in the year I spent in Goa under Luigi's guidance I acquired the kind of education I would never have got at the best European universities. It was Luigi who advised me to seek work in the Royal Hospital of Goa as an orderly.

'You have no trade, Niccolao, but all the needs of a young man. To satisfy those needs you will require money,' Luigi had smiled, hinting at the money it would cost me to visit even the cheaper brothels.

Like the rest of Goa, the Royal Hospital, once renowned all over India, had fallen on bad days. Patient care had deteriorated, as had cleanliness and the quality of medical equipment. The orderlies, mostly of mixed breed, supplemented their income by extorting money from the patients for the smallest service—giving a thirsty patient a glass of water, for instance. The food, beef tea and rice with an occasional ragout, which the orderlies shared with the patients, was terrible. But the hospital still had some expert surgeons and the year I spent there gave me the opportunity to study hundreds of patients and a variety of sicknesses from the closest quarters.

Between Luigi's careful explanations and instructions, and watching the experts at the Royal Hospital closely as they went about their daily duties, I soon mastered the routine medical procedures. I did not much care for purging. It was too easy. What skill is required in cleaning a patient's system by giving him large doses of Calomel that makes him incontinent from the mouth and the anus? Cauterizing, searing a bleeding part of the body with a hot iron or boiling oil to stop the flow of blood, did not need elaboration either. Blistering, the pouring of acid or application of hot plasters on the skin to raise blisters, which would then be drained, was more mysterious. 'The body can only contain one illness at a time,' Luigi had explained. 'When a second illness enters the body, the first one is expelled. The burn on the sick person's body forces out the original illness.'

I avoided both these procedures as much as I could. They were too violent for my peaceable Venetian nature. As was the treatment of serious illnesses such as malaria and cholera, commonplace in Goa because of its pestilential climate, by pressing a red-hot iron rod against the middle of the heel, which allays the stomach pain and stops the vomiting and other discharges. I could never get used to the smell of burning skin and the patients' screams of pain. The treatment that I adopted as my own, and which later stood me in good stead in my practice at the Mogul court, was bleeding.

Goan doctors, who have incorporated some Hindu notions and remedies in their practice, are famous all over the Indies as experts in this highly sought-after therapy. Impure blood is the root cause of many ailments and the process of bloodletting that rids it of poisons is not only recommended for fevers and inflammations but also in instances of stubborn skin diseases, tumours, gout, excessive drowsiness, and when the liver and spleen become enlarged. I remember I was fascinated by the treatment the very first time I watched one of the surgeons at the hospital, a *mestica* with a pock-marked face and smelling of feni, the palm liquor he drank in large quantities, carry out the procedure. As the attending orderly, he had asked me to take the patient, an attractive thirty-year-old woman of his own race, out into the hospital garden and make her stand in the sun for half an hour so as to make the blood flow easily. I could not but admire the extreme care with which the surgeon, none the worse for his alcoholic excesses of the previous night, first applied an antiseptic paste and then used a sharp scalpel to make superficial incisions in selected places on the woman's arm. After each incision, he examined the blood that he collected in a shallow pan. He must have made at least twenty parallel or vertical incisions on the woman's arms before he was satisfied that the dark, poisonous blood had been replaced by healthy blood, lighter in colour. I had marvelled at the doctor's technique. Not only had the woman shown no sign of pain but the cuts he had made had been so precise that the blood that collected in the pan was never more than 350 ml. To me, bloodletting was like the delicate work of a goldsmith, far superior to the blacksmithy of cauterizing and blistering.

Soon I too became proficient in the art by practising on patients who were mostly too sick or too poor to know the difference between an orderly and a real doctor. In return, I was much kinder to patients than most other orderlies who took money for the simplest of favours like bringing them water or sneaking them some confectionery. I never took money from patients, even when I helped those convalescing from bloodletting avoid drinking the three glasses of cow's urine that the hospital prescribed as mandatory. This was another remedy learnt from Hindu doctors who ascribe medical benefits to the five products of the cow—milk, curd, clarified butter, dung and urine. Whether in exchange of money or not, we orderlies emptied the glasses on the floor and the hospital always stank of cow urine.

As our friendship deepened, I discovered that Luigi was also a firm believer in Hindu medicine though he was ever so guarded when he talked of it.

'Their medicine is very different from ours,' Luigi would say, initially feigning condescension. 'In their view, the sovereign remedy for sickness is abstinence. A patient with a fever should not be given any nourishment. Nothing is considered worse for a sick body than meat broth. They believe it corrupts the stomach and worsens the illness. But most extraordinary is their conviction that bloodletting should be employed sparingly and only in extraordinary circumstances. It is recommended only when an inflammation of the chest, liver or kidneys has taken place.'

Gradually, as our friendship progressed, I discovered that Luigi's fascination for Hindu medicine had developed from his intimacy with a Hindu physician who lived in a remote village almost halfway to the border of the lands ruled by the Marathas and whom Luigi sought out whenever he travelled in those parts. His association with the Hindu doctor, whom he respectfully called Vaidraj—king of physicians—went back fifteen years. He had kept it secret so as not to be misunderstood by his Franciscan brothers. Or, worse, by the Inquisition.

'More so,' he said hesitatingly, 'because I fear he combines medicine with witchcraft.'

'Witchcraft?' I asked.

'I have seen him perform marvellous feats of diagnosis by just feeling the pulse in a patient's wrist. An experienced physician, Vaidraj tells me, can see the image of every important organ of the body reflected in the beat, movement and temperature of the pulse. But what is more astonishing—and that is where I suspect the involvement of witchcraft—is that in case of a longstanding illness, he can predict the time of the patient's death to a precise number of days or even hours.'

I was fascinated by what Luigi told me. I promised myself that one day I, too, would master the Hindu art of reading the pulse, even if it be witchcraft.

'His medicine possesses many other secrets,' Luigi continued. 'Even Mohammedan physicians at the Mogul court, followers of the rules of Avicenna and Averroes, who, like the rest of their race, generally despise the Hindus, are not averse to including some of the Hindu remedies and methods into their own practice.'

I now understood why Hindu doctors were so well regarded in Goa, even by the Portuguese. They were the rare heathens allowed to walk on the street under umbrellas carried by servants although they continued to be denied the privilege of wearing shoes. The sight of a famous physician walking barefoot while dressed in magnificent robes, followed by servants holding a richly caparisoned umbrella above him, the dignified expression on his face denying the truth revealed by his bare feet, always evoked in me a strange mix of outrage and admiration.

It was the word 'secret' that became lodged in my mind like a hook in the mouth of a fish. If I wanted to consort with nobles and princes in the capital of the Mogul empire, be remunerated in purses filled with gold *mohur*s and pearl necklaces, in place of the few silver coins reluctantly forked out by ordinary citizens for medical attention, then I needed to know the secret remedies of the *vaid*s that were still hidden from my Mohammedan and European colleagues and rivals. I began to pester Luigi to take me to meet Vaidraj. I had been in Goa for about nine months when Luigi finally agreed.

Vaidraj's village was no more than fifteen kilometres inland but it still took us the best part of a day to reach our destination. First, we travelled upstream for a couple of hours along a narrow channel that cut through a thick undergrowth of dark green mangroves which had been never penetrated by rays of the sun. Then we walked across a gently undulating plain dotted with paddy fields in all shades of brown, patiently awaiting the monsoon showers still five months away. Carefully tended groves of trees announced the existence of a few villages much before we caught a glimpse of human habitation.

Situated at the foot of a small hill, the doctor's village was larger than I had expected. Rows of mud huts with thatched roofs made from dried palm fronds, which one sees all over Goa, were broken by the occasional stone-and-mortar house with tiled roofs. A small but lively bazaar had been constructed at the centre. Almost all the vendors, squatting in the shade of torn umbrellas, their wares spread in front of them on mats woven from coconut fronds, were women. On sale were mounds of dried ginger, tamarind, lentils, jaggery, areca nuts, bunches of small yellow bananas, papayas, jars of sesame oil. Clad in red or green saris that were tied with one end pulled between the thighs and secured at the lower back and short-sleeved bodices that ended above the waist, the women gossiped loudly among themselves as they bargained with customers. In its animated, amiable chaos, though not in its skimpy offerings, the bazaar reminded me of markets in Venice.

We made our way past the bazaar to the far end of the village where Vaidraj was awaiting our arrival in the freshly swept forecourt of his hut. A basil plant, considered holy by the Hindus, had been planted in the middle of the courtyard. A step or two higher than the yard was a veranda that ran along the entire width of the house. In one corner of the yard, freshly plucked red chillies had been laid out to dry in the sun. In another corner, next to a well, was a raised mud platform under a peepul tree. This was to be our dwelling for the two days of our visit. At night, thin mattresses spread on the platform served as our beds. These were rolled up in the morning. During the day this is where we sat and spoke with Luigi's friend and where our meals were brought to us on plantain leaves.

Vaidraj's black eyes were sharp and shrewd and I could feel their scrutinizing gaze bore into me before they softened in affection as he welcomed Luigi with folded palms. As we took our seats on the platform under the peepul tree, two servants came out of the house. One carried tumblers of milky coconut water as refreshment for our dry throats. The other brought a bucket of water from the well to wash our dusty feet.

I took an instant liking to the doctor. As Vaidraj spoke to Luigi, enquiring after his health and the state of affairs in Goa, his dark eyes often turned to look upon my face. I realized why Luigi, otherwise a recluse, had warmed to him. A small, lean man in his early fifties, with close-cropped grey hair and grey stubble on his unlined cheeks, Vaidraj was dressed simply in a white cloth wrapped around his waist which came down to his knees. Except for a white cotton string looped across his torso, a sign that he had been born into a high caste, he was bare-chested. When Luigi introduced me and spoke affectionately of my dreams of making my fortune at the court of the Great Mogul, Vaidraj asked me in halting Portuguese whether I spoke Konkani, the local language. I answered in the affirmative in his own tongue and his face broke into a child-like smile. He turned to Luigi and, patting him on the shoulder, said, 'You have taught him well, my friend.' Then he turned to me. 'You want to learn about our medicine, my friend tells me.'

'Yes, if you will teach me.'

'Show me your right palm.'

Puzzled, I extended my hand. He took it gently in his own, leaned forward and peered closely at the lines on my palm. His breath smelt strongly of garlic, a purifier of blood in Hindu medicine, and I had to imperceptibly move my head to avoid its full impact.

'Yes,' he said after a while, nodding vigorously and scratching his cheek, 'you have the gift. Without it, medicines refuse to unlock their secrets. You see, it is the doctor who makes a medicine effective.'

His gaze returned to my palm and he gently traced the lines with the nail of his index finger. 'This boy is destined to make a fortune at the court,' he told Luigi. 'He will face many dangers. If he wishes I will teach him about the medicines we create for rejuvenation. They will bring him both good fortune and ill luck.'

In the euphoria of youth that closes ears to words like 'danger' or 'ill luck', I revelled in the future I discerned in his prophecy. The tropical villa became grander, the young Indian women sharing my bed more voluptuous.

Like most Hindu physicians, Luigi's friend was a palmist and a wonderful cook. The prognosis of a disease in the Hindu system of medicine depends as much on accurately deciphering the lines on the palm as on a physician's expertise in reading bodily signs. Fate determines the outcome of an illness as much as the virulence of a fever or the state of the patient's organs. Most Hindu medicine is based on the patient's intake of the correct diet for a particular illness. A doctor needs to possess extensive knowledge of the healing properties of plants and fruits and the correct preparation that would render them most effective. Take the humble coconut as an example. Young coconuts are used for almost a dozen infantile complaints such as diarrhoea and sores in the mouth. When the fruit is fully grown but still tender, its sweet water is used to good effect in the treatment of inflammation of the liver and the bladder since it increases the frequency of urination. When the nut ripens, an oil with great medicinal value is extracted from the hard coconut meat and used as a purge for the irascible since it expels bile. The oil also helps soothe ulcers and burns and reduces adipose tissue.

Later in the evening, as we lay under the stars on our mattresses, Luigi enlightened me about his friend's enigmatic offer to educate me in the medicines of 'rejuvenation'. Simply put, Vaidraj had offered to teach me the secret science of aphrodisiacs, knowledge that was much in demand among the nobility of the Mogul empire. The Omrah in the imperial court were known to possess ravenous sexual appetites, but given the number of women in their harems, their performance could never hope to match their expectations. While the Mohammedan physicians at the Great Mogul's court possessed extensive knowledge of aphrodisiacs, their potions, while increasing a man's vigour, did not especially add to his pleasure. This they left to nature, unaware that in such matters nature reveals itself best when coaxed through artifice. This was where my expertise, acquired from my new friend would come into play, should I so choose.

Having accepted Vaidraj's offer with alacrity and a becoming humility, I paid three more visits to his village after that first one. Each time I stayed with him for four days. Vaidraj first taught me the basics of reading the pulse and progressed to the examination of stool for its colour, consistency and smell to diagnose disorders of the stomach, which the Hindus regard as the root of most ailments. He was far too shrewd not to divine the real purpose of my visits. But I believe he wanted to test my patience as much as my commitment by revealing the mysteries of rejuvenation to me only during my third and last visit. The centrepiece of Vaidraj's teachings was the preparation of a potion which the woman rubs on the inner walls of her sex before intercourse. It makes lying with her exquisitely pleasurable for the man, heightening his pleasure to the point of pain. At least for a while, it stops him from going to other women.

'If you rub the ointment on the genitals of a bitch, you will see that in a couple of hours all the dogs in the neighborhood will come sniffing and try to mount it. And this when the bitch is not even on heat!' Vaidraj said.

This particular preparation gained me quite a reputation in the harems of the Mogul court, and I was careful to be very selective about my clients for its administration. But while it made me wealthy it also brought me great grief, as I shall narrate later.

Looking back at the first year I spent in India, I see that my fondness for the Hindus comes from the generosity shown to me at the beginning of my sojourn by two of their race, one a man and the other a woman. Both were my teachers, educating me in more ways than one. I have already talked of the man, Vaidraj, Luigi's friend. The woman? She was an illiterate young prostitute, no more than sixteen years old, who was as new to her profession as I was to mine. The other girls in the brothel are now only half-remembered bodies on unmade beds, but not Mala.

I was the only regular European patron of a native establishment which lay midway between the town and a Hindu village. Other Europeans, with more money, preferred a better class of brothels. The *mestica* in these houses wore long-sleeved dresses, carried painted hand fans and affected Portuguese airs. The girls in the brothel I visited were from villages in the neighbouring Maratha region. Most were in their teens or early twenties and the establishment hummed with youthful high spirits. They wore bright-coloured saris and loved to wear silver necklaces, bracelets, ankle-rings, large earrings and nose-rings. I remain grateful to those young Hindu girls, with their kohl-rimmed dark eyes, jet black hair pulled back in a high bun and wreathed in bright yellow flowers, for so generously letting me in their beds and sharing their bodies with me. Especially Mala.

As I age, the periods of reverie more welcome than those of expectation, Mala pushes herself more and more to the forefront of my awareness. I close my eyes and gaze at her as she lies naked on her stomach. I caress her smooth back, the hue of woodsmoke. She sits up and laughingly pulls my face into her lap. She runs her fingers through my curly hair, now lank and thinning. Even today, the memory of her smell can enliven my withered senses: the faint aroma of coconut oil combined with the scent of a flowery perfume that came off the sweat between her breasts. I am as one intoxicated as I nuzzle deeper into her lap. Here, the darker musk of her body struggled against being swamped by the briny odour of her female oils. At the time, to say goodbye to Mala, to never lie in her bed again with her warm body nestling against mine, was not difficult. It is only now, with age, that the thought of parting from Mala belatedly reveals the pain I did not feel then. Today, as I bend over my rosewood desk, penning these lines with the quill pen clutched between a thumb and an arthritic finger, I realize the full worth of the first teacher of my body and the two teachers of my mind.

'Indians must be among the laziest people in the world, or at least the most indifferent'

FRANCOIS BERNIER

ON A WARM DAWN, warning of the scorching day advancing in its wake, the caravan of almost a hundred wagons, carrying the most varied goods from all over the world—silver coins, glassware, and bales of velvet from Europe, musk and porcelain from China, pearls and wine from Persia, coffee from Arabia, ivory from Ethiopia—set out from Surat. Each wagon was drawn by ten or twelve oxen and guarded by four soldiers paid for by the owner of the merchandise. The Governor had put a luxuriously appointed small carriage, to which a pair of oxen had been harnessed, at my disposal. The oxen of India are small but allow themselves to be driven like our horses, trotting as easily as our hacks. As I watched a sullen sun slowly rise above the arid plain that stretched for miles in every direction, the carts ahead blurred in the dust raised by oxen hoofs, I could never have imagined that I would not only be a privileged spectator but also play a role, albeit a minor one, in the struggle for the throne of the Indies that was to soon break out between the sons of Emperor Shah Jahan.

Other than the fabled tree-lined Agra–Lahore highway, which M. Briffault had described as 'one of the best in the world', most roads in India are little more than muddy tracks that cease to exist when passing through forests and ravines. The highway from Surat to Agra and then on to Delhi is one of the main arteries of the Mogul empire. It was in much better condition than other Indian roads, although it had its share of potholes and stretches where patches of mud that had been washed away during the last rains were yet to be repaired. Rattling along on uneven ground in my light cart, covering about twenty miles a day in the white heat of the Indian sun, the first week of travel was trying, especially since the canteen of wine which the Governor had thoughtfully included in my provisions did not offer the refreshment of body and spirit I had hoped it would when the caravan halted for the night at a serai. On the second day itself the heat and the constant jolting had turned the wine into no more than expensive vinegar!

The serais, where we sought shelter at the end of a day's travel, are inns strategically located on the highway outside towns or large villages in order to allow travellers to camp in safety. The gates of a serai close at sundown with the watchman's announcement that everyone must look after his belongings and picket his horses and oxen by their fore and hind legs. At sunrise, the watchman once again shouts out three warnings for everyone to check his belongings. The gates are opened if no theft is reported. In case there has been a theft, a thorough search is carried out till the thief is discovered, and the poor wretch is promptly strung up from the branch of a tree outside the serai. Some of the serais, such as the one built by the Great Mogul's eldest daughter sixty miles from the city of Surat, are spacious, fortified enclosures of stone or brick, with a central courtyard encircled by arcaded chambers that can lodge up to a thousand travellers along with their horses, camels and carriages. Most serais, however, are groups of fifty or sixty thatched huts enclosed by a wall or by hedges. A few are but large, odorous barns, raised and paved all round, where human beings mingle with their animals. In summer, these barns are hot and suffocating while in winter nothing but the body heat and breath of so many animals saves the inmates from dying of the cold.

The traveller has to provide his own bedding but can buy his food from idolater men and women attached to the serai. The meal normally consists of khichri, a mess of rice and lentils boiled together and flavoured with mild spices and onions fried in ghee, which is hugely relished by the idolaters. Save for the heat that gradually worsened in the course of the day and the native khichri, which is frankly quite inedible and took me a while to get accustomed to, I can say that travelling in India is no less convenient than journeying either in France or Italy.

The tedium I would have felt of travelling alone was lightened on the very first evening when Afzal, a handsome, young Mohammedan merchant, with skin whose smoothness would have been the envy of our Parisian ladies of noble birth, decided to attach himself to me. Speaking in fluent Persian, he informed me that he was travelling with the caravan till Burhanpur, one of the larger towns on the road to Agra. Here, he intended to buy the excellent cloth, scarlet and white and of an exceeding fineness, from which women's head-dresses and veils are made and which enjoys a big market in Persia, Turkey and Armenia. He had made the journey from Surat to Burhanpur eleven times before, and I was grateful to have someone so appealing to the eye and so knowledgeable about the land explain its sights and make sense of the many curious incidents that occurred on the way, which would otherwise baffle any foreign traveller.

Afzal, the first Mohammedan I met and whom I quickly grew fond of, was a man of good humour, fond of witticisms (not all of which I understood) and, like most others of his race, possessed a tendency towards flights of fancy that I found more enchanting than tedious. As we sat together companionably after the evening meal, the water in the bowl of his hukka gurgling every time he drew in the smoke with a loud, satisfied whoosh, we talked about what had struck me as curious during the day's travel. Afzal would provide a context to my impressions, offer his own opinions and elaborate further on related matters, some interesting, others not.

The conversation was not one-sided, however, with me playing the student asking questions and Afzal reacting as a teacher would. I, too, had the satisfaction of correcting some of his misconceptions about Europe and Europeans. Afzal believed that Europeans live on islands and that it is only at sea that they are proficient in battle and are formidable opponents. His impression of Europeans, '*farangis*' as the Indians call them, was derived from those who serve in the artillery of the Moguls and with whom the natives are most familiar. The *farangis* are devoid of all fear of God, he said. They take eight to ten wives, are constantly drunk, have no occupation but gambling, and are eager to cheat whomsoever they can. Their morals are much worse than those of the Mohammedans, or even of the idolaters, since for small monetary considerations they are willing to abandon their faith and convert to the religion of Mohammed. These Europeans are Christians only in name, I hastened to correct him. Most people in Europe are as God-fearing as any Mohammedan. Some may occasionally drink to excess or succumb to other all-too-human weaknesses but, then, was this not true of any race?

'Ah, yes, Bernier,' Afzal said agreeably, his voice pleasingly gravelled from the smoke, 'we are all creatures of God. We are all human, more human than otherwise. Allah the Merciful will forgive our failings.'

I knew that as a Mohammedan to whom all intoxicants are forbidden, he struggled against his addiction to bhang, a beverage made from leaves of dried hemp ground to powder and soaked in water, and normally drunk by poor people who do not have enough money to procure alcoholic spirits. He was a generous man, this Afzal, who never let me pay for our dinners at the serais, but then generosity towards people they like—and they are quick to decide on their likes and dislikes—seems to be one of the more attractive features of the followers of Mohammed.

At the beginning of our travel, the land was of mixed character, sometimes covered with woods and sometimes with fields of wheat and rice. Although most of the rivulets were now dry, we had difficulty fording others because of the stones and rocks under the water that could overturn a wagon if the driver was not careful. As we approached Burhanpur, the road became better. Each day, we came across brooks with fresh water, shady and pleasant woods filled with deer, gazelles, wild oxen and a variety of birds. I was tempted by the opportunity to hunt with the matchlock M. Briffault had given me as a farewell present, but Afzal warned me not to stray away from the road because of the presence of robbers in the woods, who lay in wait of any unwary traveller who was unable to resist this temptation.

The caravan rested in Burhanpur for two days and Afzal graciously offered to show me around the town rather than immediately attend to his business. Burhanpur is a medium-sized town on the bank of a river with good, clear water but without fortifications. Its crumbling monuments and the general air of neglect and decay, which I had also seen in a couple of other towns where we camped for more than a day instead of the night halts at serais that were our normal resting place, reinforced the impression I had gathered from Surat that Indians must be among the laziest people in the world, or at least the most indifferent. For although more people in India live in towns than in Europe, the urban landscape appears desolate and its imminent decay is distressing to the discerning European eye. Gardens, mansions, palaces are kept in repair only so long as the owner is alive. Once he is dead no one will care for what he built. Each succeeding generation tries to erect buildings of its own, utterly disregarding the labours of its ancestors, with the result that roads leading to cities and towns, as indeed many areas of a city itself, are strewn with fallen columns of stone. It is a miracle how any monument that is not a temple or a mosque has managed to survive more than two to three generations in this country.

On the first morning of our stay in Burhanpur, while walking around the market which was well stocked with fresh fruit like oranges, lemons and mangos and plenty of fresh vegetables, we were witness to an amusing spectacle. In contrast to idolaters, Mohammedans wear beards. The new governor of Burhanpur, a scrupulous observer of the Faith, had issued an edict that no Mohammedan should wear a beard longer than four finger-breadths and had appointed an official to enforce the regulation. Each morning, this official sallied forth in the company of his attendants and soldiers to measure the beards he came across on the street and, if necessary, to trim them to the required length. It was entertaining to see the official and his men running around in the market, laying hold of men by the beards in order to measure them and clip off the excess. They would also run a razor over an incipient moustache to uncover the lips, so that when pronouncing the name of Allah, there would be no impediment to the sound ascending straight to heaven.

On the following day, I was sorry to part with Afzal whom I now regarded as a friend. He had made my journey informative and agreeable. He appeared hurt when I refused his farewell gift of a night at the town's best bordello to seal our friendship.

'Perhaps you would prefer a boy, Bernier? I can wager that our boys are better than your European lads. They know how to tighten their sphincter muscles at the right time,' he tried again.

I had had no such experience with a European boy and had no desire to have one with an Indian lad, I told him, declining the fresh offer. It is true, however, that teenaged Indian boys, with their silky nut-brown skin, bright black eyes, flashing white teeth and lissome limbs make an attractive sight and can be tempting to men with un-Christian inclinations.

The rest of the journey to Agra was uneventful in that we were neither set upon by brigands nor delayed for long on account of being detained on the way by one of the Great Mogul's governors demanding, as is their habit, inordinately large bribes to let goods pass through his domain. For the last one hundred miles or so, right up to our destination, the caravan passed among fertile fields which strongly resembled the Beausse plain around Chartres. I noticed that without Afzal as a guide to inform and explain, and in the manner of all first-time travellers to a strange country, I, too, allayed my nervousness (of which I was not aware at the time) by concentrating on features of the land that were similar to those at home, while my eyes quickly passed over sights to which I was unaccustomed and which could have disturbed my equanimity. It also helped that the villages were close to each other, making travel more comfortable since there was little hurry to reach a particular serai before sunset when the towns and serais close their gates and do not allow any one to either enter or leave.

Twenty-seven days after setting out from Surat, I arrived in Delhi on the evening of the twenty-fifth day of April, 1657.

I HAD, FROM THE time of my arrival in India, regarded my stay in Goa as a prologue to the main act of my life, and so while I left Goa in haste it was not with a heavy heart. I knew that the time was upon me to venture out into the larger world. I was certain that glory awaited me with a certain foot-tapping impatience.

My detractors have spread many stories about my hurried departure from Goa, but there is no truth in them. That I was having an affair with Don Braganza's wife is a despicable lie. Would a lady of such fine sensibilities as Dona Cristina tie a string to her toe each night before going to bed and hang the other end out of the window for me to tug at at midnight to check if the coast was clear for a quick rendezvous in the garden shed? Would she, like an ordinary village wench, be caught in *flagrante delicto* in the shed one night by her husband who had chosen that night to drink less wine than was his stuporous wont and reached out across his bed to find his wife missing from his side? And what of the preposterous story about me having fled across the garden and into the street with not a thread on my body, being chased by Don Braganza's Kaffirs firing their blunderbusses in the direction of my rapidly retreating posterior? Lies, lies, fanciful lies! If these stories had even a grain of truth, Dona Cristina's husband would not have left her alive. Nor would I have been able to leave Goa as easily as I did. I left in a hurry, true, but certainly not in headlong panic.

The truth is a less tawdry tale, easily told. Dona Cristina's favourite maid was recovering from a severe bout of malarial fever in the Royal Hospital and the lady often dropped by to enquire after her well-being. One day I bumped into Dona Cristina just when I was carrying the maid's regulation glass of *pissat vache* to be poured out into the ground. The glass tilted and drops of the liquid fell on the sleeve of her silk dress. Dona Cristina took a step back, her nostrils flaring enchantingly in disgust at the smell of urine. I stuttered an apology and stepped aside to let her pass. Surprised by the unusual sight of a European among the low-born *mestica* orderlies, the intended words of chastisement did not reach her lips. Instead, she smiled. I smiled in return. In the next week, we exchanged formal greetings whenever we passed each other. Eventually, one afternoon, she accosted me in the corridor and invited me to sit out with her on a bench in the unkempt hospital garden. This wooden bench, with two broken slats and covered with pigeon droppings, was to become our regular meeting place three times a week over the next four weeks, until her maid was discharged from the hospital. A plump and attractive woman in her early thirties, Cristina Braganza had the kindest eyes, and an even more gentle heart. I found it easy to respond to her gentle questioning. It felt more like an invitation to share the story of my young life than an idle probing animated by curiosity. The experience of unburdening my soul, pouring out my old pains and my newborn hopes into the ears of a sympathetic woman was so novel for a motherless boy that I fell a little in love with her, never of the carnal kind. At the time, Mala was the only woman who could stoke the fire of those particular promptings. If Dona Cristina had any carnal feelings towards me, she either hid them well or signalled them so subtly that I remained oblivious to them.

I was aware of the danger of conversing with a married woman in her husband's absence—Don Braganza was then away on a military campaign—yet I could not resist visiting Dona Cristina at home after her maid was cured. My need to be in her presence had turned into an addiction. Don Braganza was uncertain about the extent of my intimacy with his wife when he returned. Otherwise, there wouldn't have been two Kaffirs waiting for me at the gate of the hospital with a signed note from him commanding me to leave Goa within three days. I would have been confronted, instead, by a jealous army captain with a raised sword or a cocked gun ready to drive the blade through me or fire a bullet into my head.

I never saw Dona Cristina again. On the morning of my departure, her maid brought me a letter. The letter was addressed to her cousin Maria Escobar, a Portuguese woman who had been among those captured by the Mogul forces during their siege of Hoogly. She now held a position of import in the crown prince Dara Shukoh's harem, and Dona Cristina had often spoken fondly of her to me. At first, I resisted opening the letter. But curiosity about what she had to say about me soon triumphed over my scruples. In the letter, Dona Cristina had recommended me in the highest terms as an accomplished physician, especially in the arts of rejuvenation. She had chosen her words carefully to hide the tenderness she felt towards me. Instead, she had encoded her feelings in a familiar perfume lightly sprayed on the back of the envelope.

Here I must confess to the biggest shame of my life, one which has haunted me for more than twenty years now. In the self-centered preoccupation of youth, as I was leaving Goa I did not think twice about snapping ties with people who had cherished and helped me: Mala, Luigi, Vaidraj. Love and gratitude, sadness at the parting of ways, the pain of loss, were parts of me that I had excised with my eye upon a distant star. They have begun to emerge and demand a hearing now when I am older, and perhaps wiser, and have discovered how cold the star of ambition actually is. At the time, I was dry-eyed and drier-hearted when I bid goodbye to Luigi and Vaidraj, my two benefactors. Mala I did not visit to bid farewell. How monstrous is the youth of men!

Armed only with the letter of introduction to Maria Escobar, but with full faith in my ability to both charm and cure (the two indispensable ingredients of a doctor's success), I arrived in the new imperial capital of Delhi on 15 June 1654, two months and eleven days after leaving Goa.

Ah, Delhi! Anyone who has been in Delhi in the heat of June shall be well prepared to face the fires of hell. Hell may be hotter, but it certainly does not experience the mistral the Indians call the loo. This hot wind, heavy with gritty sand that can make sandpaper out of eyelids, can arise at any time of the day or night during the months of May and June, causing the city to barricade itself behind closed shutters for most part of the day and awaken to life once the sun has set. Early mornings and evenings thus became the hours for my explorations of the imperial capital.

On the second morning after my arrival, I sought out the house of the four Jesuit fathers whom Luigi had once mentioned while enlightening me on missionary undertakings in India. Like his father, the irredeemably irreligious Emperor Jahangir who encouraged Jesuit priests only for the amusement of watching them squabble with the mullahs, the Great Mogul, too, had no use for Jesuits. There were none left in the city except for Father Buze, a Flemish priest, the German Father Roth, my fellow Italian, the Neapolitan, Father Malpica, and the Portuguese Father Juzarte, whom I never met since he had gone on a long visit to Goa. The Jesuits enjoyed the protection of the eldest of Emperor Shah Jahan's sons, Dara Shukoh, known to be a keen student of religions and an enthusiastic practitioner of the mystical Sufi strain of Islam, and were his informants on all matters of Christian faith. My plan was to ask for Father Malpica's help in reaching Maria Escobar in Prince Dara's harem.

Father Malpica turned out to be friendly middle-aged man who did not resemble any Jesuit I had known. For one, he was not dressed as a man of cloth but in a white cotton churidar and a calf-length fine muslin *qaba* of the same colour. The *qaba* was fashionably tight at the torso but loose from the waist down. It was tied in the front on the left, as Hindus tie their garments, rather than on the right in the manner of the Muslims. His fleshy chest and the bulge of an ample belly straining against the diaphanous material of the tunic did not exactly bespeak of the austere lifestyle for which the Jesuits are known and respected. Having listened gravely to my request for his assistance, the Father said, 'I will help you myself. I, too, have a certain influence with the prince. But to do that I need to know more about your professional expertise. You look very young to me.'

I recounted an edited version of my story, one which exaggerated my medical skills and embellished the nature and length of my medical experience as a physician. I even added to my account a couple of histories of successful cures of difficult cases which I had heard from Luigi.

'Good! I needed to make sure, although the recommendation speaks for itself. Such is the faith of Indians in European medicine that many shameless quacks have begun to hover around the native courts,' Father Malpica said after I finished, his small, dark eyes kind but shrewd. 'Come and see me after a week and I may have some news for you.'

For the next three days, I explored the city in the early mornings and its people late in the evenings. Both are delightful as long as they are encountered on their own terms and not judged by European standards. Delhi's public buildings and spaces are magnificent. One of the most pleasing vistas is of the avenue that begins from the Agra gate and ends at the emperor's citadel. This is a long and spacious street, divided in the middle by a canal of running water. Both sides of the street are lined with raised pathways, five to six feet high and four feet broad. Petty officials of the state sit here and go about their functions without being inconvenienced by the traffic of people, horses, carriages and oxen carts that pass below.

The dwellings of common people may seem like wretched huts but their mud floors and walls and thatched roofs are well suited for Delhi's hot climate. They are airy and are swept clean more than once during the day. They are free of the filth and foul smell of the poorer quarters of Venice where people blithely dump dirty water out on the cobblestones. The Indians, even the poor, bathe regularly and the smell of sweat, inevitable in a people living in a hot climate, is of fresh and not stale perspiration. It is true the common people are poverty-stricken and sorely oppressed. But they have neither lost their zest for life nor an essential kindness.

In the evenings my habit was to wander through the bazaars of Delhi and visit its eateries or taverns. It struck me, as it had in Goa, that Indians, whether Hindu or Muslim, are unfailingly courteous and often generous beyond their means. Guests are like gods, the Hindus believe, and Muslims share the sentiment although they would recoil from its expression in words that reek of idolatry. Save for a trifling amount spent on buying a couple of flatbreads and yoghurt for my daily morning meals, I did not spend a pice on food and drink during those days. And not a night passed when I was not hosted in one of the illegal taverns that dotted the city, drinking spirits being forbidden by Islamic law but tolerated under the benign influence of the Wali Ahad.

Outside the taverns, free entertainment was available in the public squares. Child acrobats, some aged six or seven, turned somersaults to the accompaniment of drums beaten by their fathers or elder brothers. Bears with strings drawn through their noses were made to perform ponderous dance steps by their handlers. Monkeys on long leashes and dressed in men's trousers or women's skirts played out domestic quarrels. Just as on the streets of Venice, charlatans shouted out the virtues of the medicines they peddled. But whereas in the city of my birth cures for pox or ague, boils or plague, were the most touted, in Delhi the peddlers who drew the largest crowds promised potency to men, fertility to women and a reversal of the ravages of age to both.

I must confess that it was not the jugglers and the mountebanks that held my attention on most evenings, but the dancing girls with their amazingly supple bodies. I would watch them, mesmerized, as they gyrated or glided across the hastily constructed wooden stages lit by many torches, luring men with their kohl-lined eyes and graceful, sensual movements. Later, I would visit the quarter where the girls lived. They would be standing outside their huts with a candle glowing like a yolk of light in the window, a sign that they were ready to receive clients. Youth pounded through my veins, peremptory in its demands. I picked the girls at random, never repeating my choice. I had no wish to become attached. Mala still ruled my memory, if not my unruly body.

On the fourth day, in the early hours of the morning, I was summoned by Father Malpica.

'I have a message from Maria Escobar for you, Niccolao,' he said. 'You are to immediately proceed to the house of Prince Dara's minister, Wazir Khan. His first wife is seriously ill. The doctors who have treated her until now have all declared her condition as hopeless. The prince's chief hakim has gone so far as to say that he will burn all his books and become the disciple of any man who can cure her. Maria has persuaded the minister that you be given a chance. Wazir Khan did ask my opinion and I have strongly supported your case. Now it is up to you.'

I mounted the horse sent for me and made my way to Wazir Khan's house with considerable apprehension. I fully understood that both Maria Escobar and Father Malpica would wish to test me before recommending my appointment to the prince's court. I was grateful, but silently cursed them for setting me a severe test in which failure was almost certain.

In comparison to the vast harems kept by many Omrah, Wazir Khan's harem consisted of only four wives and less than a dozen concubines. The latter were more for the purpose of public display since the minister's sexual energies were fully exhausted in his obsession for a twelve-year-old page in his service, as I would soon be told. Father Malpica had warned me that like all harems, this one, too, would be strictly guarded by eunuchs, its access barred to all men except Wazir Khan. The only exceptions to this are male physicians, and that too only when an inmate is too sick to be taken to the gate to be examined.

The harem lay in the centre of Wazir Khan's mansion and I had to cross two large courtyards and a garden lined with cypress trees to reach it. Maria Escobar was waiting for me at the gate accompanied by the Aitmad, the head eunuch of the harem. She greeted me briskly, betraying no hint of our Goa connection. In my anxiety all I could register of her presence was a compact body and a competent manner before the Aitmad threw a shawl over my head, covering my face. Taking me roughly by the hand, he led me through the gate of the harem while Maria walked behind me. Peering through the weaves of the shawl, I saw that on three sides of a courtyard tiled with red sandstone were rows of apartments with no windows, their door-like openings screened by curtains. These, I gathered, were where the women lived. From the smell of spices and a clamour of voices behind me, I deduced that the kitchen and the quarters for the *darogha*s, the middle-aged matronly supervisors of the harem, were on the fourth side. At the mention of 'harem', our European imaginations continue to be inflamed with images of nubile women in diaphanous attire that flare at the hips and are tight around ankles, seductive women who recline languidly on soft divans awaiting the entry of their lord and master. But on that first visit to a real harem all I was aware of was the mid-morning emptiness of its verandas, with no more than six or seven *darogha*s squatting listlessly or dozing off on the floor in front of the apartments .

When the shawl was removed I found myself before a thin curtain stretched across the middle of a room. Behind it was the indistinct silhouette of a woman lying on a bed. This was my patient. Hushed female voices whispered on the other side of the curtain.

Maria was now standing next to me. She recited the history of the woman's sickness in halting Persian spoken with a familiar Portuguese lilt, punctuating almost every sentence with a respectful nod and the address of 'Doctor'. Gently, she guided my examination of the patient.

'Yes, of course, Doctor, you need to examine the pulse first,' she said, directing my hand behind the curtain to place it on the woman's wrist. The pulse was irregular and very weak. 'She was restless during the week but has been almost comatose since yesterday,' Maria continued. 'There have been three sessions of bloodletting but they have only weakened her further.'

My apprehension mounted as she recited the woman's symptoms, a rather long list of woes that I racked my brain to fit to a familiar disease. Then, as though a lifeline had been thrown to me, I heard the word 'stool' and quickly enquired about the patient's bowel movements.

'No, doctor,' Maria replied, 'she has not relieved herself for days together.'

This was sufficient information. Just as a poet sometimes feels his poetry has come from the music of the stars and is not of his own making, a doctor too has moments of inspiration when a disease and its treatment are laid out clearly before him.

'She immediately needs to be administered a clyster,' I pronounced with supreme confidence.

Muslims have strong objections to this particular method of treatment but there was no alternative if the woman's life had to be saved. Murmurs of consternation arose behind the curtain. Maria was called inside and a message was sent to Wazir Khan. His reply that the decision lay with the women resulted in further rounds of consultation and debate. Maria finally overrode them by quoting from the Quran, '*Agar zarurat bayad, rawa bakshhad*', which she later told me roughly translates as 'necessity knows no law'. I was impressed as much by her knowledge of the Quran as by the authority in her voice. Silence descended behind the curtain as Maria emerged and gave me a triumphant smile. I smiled in answer, as much from relief as to salute her status in the harem.

'Come to Father Malpica's house in the afternoon. I will then give you all that is needed for the application,' I said.

Among the many lessons from the Hindu doctor that had been engraved in my memory was a statement he repeated often, 'The stomach is the seat of many diseases, especially ones that seem puzzling at first.' Hindus are fascinated with the journey of food through the body, by what is taken in through the mouth, what happens to it as it travels through the stomach and the intestines, and what is ejected through the rectum. For Hindus, defecation is a serious matter, requiring undivided attention and deep thought. I know of no other people who pay so much attention to the subject of gas in the intestines, or to the form, colour and consistency of stools. The inability to defecate even for a day is considered as bad as a minor illness and people habitually observe their stools to see whether they are as they should be, soft and even a little runny. My difficulty in this case was that though I remembered the ingredients of at least six enemas in Hindu medicine—I had administered a few myself at the Royal Hospital in Goa—I was not quite sure of the proportions to be prescribed. I thus took a risk (allowed Providence to guide my hand, as Father Malpica later said) and prepared a concoction out of mallows, wild endives, bran, jaggery, rock salt, olive oil and *canna fistula*. Father Malpica was immensely helpful in sending his servants running off to various bazaars to procure the ingredients. Then came the difficulty of finding an instrument with which to administer the injection. In the end, I fashioned one myself from a cow's udder fastened to one end of a hollow bamboo water pipe through which the Muslims smoke their hukkas. I corked the other end of the tube and filled the udder with the concoction.

When Maria arrived at the Jesuit house some four hours later, I handed the contraption to her, together with instructions on how to inject the enema. On Father Malpica's advice I also asked her to announce in the harem that if the enema failed to take effect within three hours the patient had no hope of living. If the patient should die, I could say I had foretold the result. This would ward off a potentially fatal blow to my reputation as a doctor. We then prayed to God and waited anxiously for news. The future I had dreamt of ever since the day I sailed from Venice hinged on the outcome of this case. A doctor's reputation can be as easily snatched away as it can be made. A good cure at the start of his professional life is sufficient to bring a doctor great credit, even if the cure be accidental. On the other hand, an initial failure, even if the doctor is learned and not at fault, prevents him from being esteemed ever again.

I had no cause to worry, however. I should have known that my star would not let me down. Within a couple of hours, Maria ran into the house, flushed and excited, and hugged me in a great show of affection.

'She has begun to mend, Niccolao! After I gave her the enema, she had a huge motion, voiding pellets as hard as camel dung with great violence. She has already begun to talk and recognize others.'

Proud and elated, I told Maria to feed the patient light chicken broth for five days. She was standing close to me and for the first time I became aware of the utterly captivating odour of her body: the strong but hardly unpleasant smell of her perspiration almost overpowering the fragrance of the rose attar to which Maria was partial. I now noticed that she was an exceptionally handsome woman in a swarthy, Portuguese way and that her green eyes flashed emerald fires when she was excited. The discovery that at times the apparent restraint of her body could melt into a wanton fluidity that would be the envy of the best dancing girls at the imperial court was to come later.

'You think the Wali Ahad will send for me?'

'Don't worry, Niccolao,' she said. 'It is done. I will tell everyone that though young in years, you are the possessor of many secret medicines known to you alone, even ones which are capable of reviving the dead.' She laughingly added, 'And not just the physical dead but also dead desires, as my cousin tells me in her letter.'

I smiled, acknowledging our complicity and saluting the beginning of our bond. The very next day, two men clad in the blue and green livery of the Wali Ahad knocked at the door of my house. I had been commanded to present myself to the prince that evening at his riverside palace, the Manzil-i-Nigambodh.

'That most excellent and learned man of Asia'

FRANCOIS BERNIER

'IT IS THE UNCERTAINTIES that energize life,' my mentor M. Gassendi had once remarked. 'Look at them as a joy rather than as a curse and you will penetrate to the heart of life's mystery . . . and grace.'

I have not experienced the truth of this statement more acutely than in the time I spent in the service of that most excellent and learned man of Asia, Danishmand Khan. Entrusted with the task of administering the empire's foreign affairs by the monarch, who reposed full trust in him, Danishmand Khan, M. Briffault had said, was one of the few nobles who was more committed to the welfare of the empire than to increasing his wealth or promoting his self-interest. After eleven years of close association, I can unhesitatingly vouch for the truth of M. Briffault's observation and can only marvel at my good fortune that I found service with a man whose character was also devoid of vanity and moral blindness, the two other forces that drive men in public life, in any society.

I noticed soon after I joined his services that Danishmand Khan, whom I was instructed upon arrival to address as Agha, master, was the only grandee who was exempt from appearing every day at the imperial court, a freedom granted in consequence of his being a man of letters who needed time to devote to his studies and to foreign affairs. He could no more dispense with his philosophical studies in the afternoon than avoid allocating the mornings to his weighty duties. But on Wednesdays he attended court in the same manner as any other Amir. This was the only time the Agha wore churidar breeches of coloured silk rather than starched white cotton. His *qaba*, the tunic worn by all Indians of a certain social standing, in which he wrapped his lean frame with the slightly rounded shoulders of the scholar, was also of silk with a floral pattern rather than of white Dacca muslin embroidered in the arabesque pattern he usually favoured. His beard, clipped to the breadth of four fingers, was always neatly combed. Unlike older Omrah, who seek to appear youthful no matter how advanced their age, he never dyed his beard nor plucked out its sprinkling of white hair. I was quite flattered when the chief eunuch of his court once said to me, 'Bernier, you do not have a beard, nor the, Agha's colouring, but you look remarkably similar to the Agha, not in features but in form.'

Like his other employees, I would go to his house every morning to mark my attendance, my brief appearance consisting of nothing more than making the ritual salaam, bowing deeply from the waist while raising my right hand to my forehead. A man of the most polished manners, Danishmand Khan was so civil and courteous that he addressed everybody, even his employees as 'janaab', sir. He disapproved of coarse language as he did of any display of anger. In Surat, after I had received the summons to reach Delhi, M. Briffault had recounted some incidents he had heard of to prepare me for my future post. It was said that Danishmand Khan's sensibilities were so refined that once when his horse stopped to answer the call of nature, he immediately dismounted and took a seat in the palanquin that was always a part of his entourage, cloaking the distaste caused by the sight, smell and sound of the horse's evacuation by claiming that his back was hurting and needed support. Again, when the architect appointed to build his mansion had shown him the plans for approval, he had studied them with much interest, making specific enquiries about the various sections. Not quite able to fathom a particular set of markings, he asked the architect about their purpose and upon being informed that they indicated the place where the lavatories would be situated, Danishmand Khan held his nostrils with his right hand and puckering up his face in disgust signalled with his left for the architect to take the plan away, as if the paper gave off an offensive odour merely because of the drawing. At the time, I had found the stories amusing, but now, after meeting him, I no longer saw them as eccentricities but as manifestations of an exquisitely refined temperament.

I got to know the Agha well through the conversations we had in his house in the evenings. Once he was free from dealing with affairs of state, the Agha would slip into the more comfortable loose *shalwar* and *qaba* after ungirding the cummerbund and send a message that he desired my company for diversion and, perhaps, instruction. Still curious as a child in spite of his fifty-odd years, Danishmand Khan gave me to understand that he would welcome discourses on the philosophies of Gassendi and Descartes, as also on the discoveries of Harvey and Pecquet in anatomy. It was at the Agha's suggestion that I began to translate Descartes's *Discourse on the Method of Properly Conducting One's Reason and of Seeking the Truth in Sciences* into Persian, an undertaking that has afforded me much satisfaction over the years. Were it not for the Agha's constant enquiries as to its progress, I might, in fact, have broken faith with the project.

Besides philosophy, Danishmand Khan enjoyed discussions about religion. Although he was dedicated to the preservation and strengthening of Islam in India, I can personally vouch that he was not a bigot and embraced a liberal view of his faith. Later, when we came closer, I enjoyed our good-humoured arguments on which religion, Christian or Mohammedan, was superior. Even when he teased me with sly provocations, smiling all the while, I was always careful not to cross the boundary that separates the Agha from his retainer, although in my case this deference did not have its origin in the disparity of our positions in the world, but arose from my genuine respect for his person and accomplishments.

Danishmand Khan's house, reflecting his character, was more sober than those of other high-ranking Omrah. It was airy, exposed on all sides to the wind, especially to the northern breezes, and had a number of terraces where the family slept on hot summer nights. The terraces opened into a large chamber where the bedsteads were moved in case it rained, or if the sleeping family was surprised by a dust storm at night, or wished to prevent paralysing numbness in the limbs caused by penetrating dews at certain times in the year. Unlike most Omrah who imitated the king in building their mansions with rare pink stone and marble from the mines of Rajputana, the Agha's house was made of ordinary brick, slaked lime and timber. The person of its owner, his modesty and understated elegance, was not obvious in the materials he had used in its construction, or in the ostentation of its furnishings, but in the attention he lavished on the gardens and the care he took in selecting the best artists from the emperor's *karkhana* to paint the murals on the walls. The walls of the entrance hall, the waiting area for a visitor, for instance, were painted by no less an artist than the renowned Mirza Kalam whose reputation extended as far as Turkey. The paintings of hunting scenes with huntsmen bearing bows and arrows or firing matchlocks at leaping tigers showed excellent skill in colour and craftsmanship, though I must admit that by being repeated on one panel after another they did appear monotonous to the eye.

Other than jade and porcelain vases and exquisite flower-pots of blue pottery from China, displayed in niches of different shapes and sizes cut into the walls, the rooms were bare of decoration. Visitors sat on thin mattresses spread on the floor that were covered with fine cotton cloth with floral designs produced by a combination of dyeing, printing and free-hand painting. Large cushions, embroidered with satin thread rather than the gold and silver brocade favoured by the Omrah, were thrown across the room. A small mattress with a fine silk covering was spread against one wall, intended for the master of the house and any person of quality who happened to call on him, or

indeed anyone else Danishmand Khan invited to share it with him. I
felt honoured that he bestowed this signal mark of favour on me quite
early in our association.

Danishmand Khan's pride was the large garden surrounding
the mansion. The pavilion located at its centre was an ideal spot for
the Agha and his friends to spend summer evenings, contemplating
or conversing. The pavilion was surrounded by a pool created from
two water channels that crossed each other, dividing the garden into
four quarters and cooling the air scented by fragrant night-flowering
plants such as jasmine, narcissus and Queen of the Night. A Mogul
garden lacks the austere beauty of our French gardens but one cannot
deny that it possesses a singular charm. The philosophical basis of a
French garden, as M. Gassendi eloquently put it, is the subordination
of nature to human reason. The control of nature is not only apparent
in the geometric designs in accordance with rules of proportion,
perspective and taste, and the attempt to create a shape as pure as
the path of the sun, but also in the aviaries and menageries that are a
part of every great French garden. In contrast, I found that a Mogul
garden endeavoured to create a reflection of the Quranic images of
Paradise; its quadrangular layout, called Chahar Bagh, an imitation of
the four paradisiacal gardens described in the Quran. Cool pavilions,
flowing springs, gushing fountains, shade and fruit trees mentioned
in the Quranic descriptions of Paradise, were its essential features.
Cypress and flowering fruit trees were planted along the main axis
of the Agha's garden to emphasize its general lines. Peonies, jasmine,
carnations, roses, pink delphiniums and hollyhocks were planted
parallel to the two principal water channels and also bordered the
smaller subdivisions of Chahar Bagh. In the spring, there would be
beds of lily, tulip, poppy, anemone, cyclamen, iris and violet.

When our familiarity grew and the Agha gained confidence in my
taste and judgement, he explained to me the underlying symbolism of
the plants and their placement in the garden. Cypress, an evergreen,
represented eternity to the Moguls, although in Persia it was also a
conventional symbol of female beauty. Flowering fruit trees such as

lemon, orange, plum, white kachnar and almond represented renewal, a symbol of youth and life.

'The *hayat bakhsh*, the life-bestowing garden, Bernier, is to a building as the soul is to the body and the lamp to an assembly,' he told me. 'Each of the water cascades you see is the whitener of the dawn. I see each fountain as a hand of light reaching out to the inhabitants of the heavens, as a string of bright pearls made to descend to reward the inhabitants of earth.' Danishmand Khan could wax lyrical when the occasion so demanded.

Each of Danishmand Khan's four wives had a separate apartment in the seraglio, where she lived with fifteen to twenty slave girls. I had heard it said that unlike the Agha, whose interest in worldly possessions was only of an aesthetic nature, his wives vied with each other in adorning their apartments with expensive ornamental flourishes. Their bedsteads were lavishly inlaid with gold and silver and their table service and utensils made extensive use of these precious metals. Because of the small size of his seraglio—the concubines normally kept for the master's added pleasures of the bed were not a part of it—Danishmand Khan needed only four eunuchs to keep watch over the women's quarters. Khwaja Chisti, the head eunuch of the Agha's seraglio, became my friend in strange circumstances which I will describe later in the narrative.

The mansions of the Omrah are exclusively oriented to provide pleasure to their owners and the seraglio plays a key role in this. Indeed, if it were not for the compulsion to attend court, no Amir would willingly leave the company of the women in his seraglio, all of them eager to satisfy every whim of his flesh. (Except, of course, for the pleasures of pederasty to which a few Omrah were known to be quite partial.) Europeans will be hard-pressed to imagine the varied delights on offer in the mansions of the Omrah or envisage the magnificence of the settings in which they are proffered.

The pleasures of the seraglio are, however, attended by the constant danger of one or the other woman going astray—and punishments for sexual misconduct of women among Mogul nobility are extreme, a starving rat placed in the trousers of the unchaste woman being the mildest. Usually the woman is put to death, the deed carried out by a family member, a brother or father, summoned for the purpose, an act that is commended rather than questioned. If I were of a more fanciful nature, I would say that I have smelt the blood of murdered women in the mansion of many an Amir.

It was not just the location of the house—situated as it was in a nondescript suburb rather than on the riverbank, the site preferred by most Omrah—or its modest construction that made Danishmand Khan's dwelling different. The distinction lay in its ambience of serenity, a quality that was generally missing from the mansions of the Mogul nobility. I can say this now with a measure of confidence, although it did take me a long time to identify the root of this subtle difference, which I could sense but not name in the beginning.

Unlike the nobility in France, the Omrah are not members of ancient families. Since all of the land belongs to the emperor, dukedoms or marquisates do not exist in India, and after an Amir's death the family's distinction is soon lost. No Amir can bequeath his title or the land assigned to him by the emperor to an heir, nor is an heir allowed to inherit the wealth of his father. Unless an Amir succeeds in obtaining a special royal favour during his lifetime for the advancement of his children, his sons, or at least his grandsons, are generally reduced to the ranks of the poor and compelled to enlist as mere troopers in the cavalry of some other Amir, although the emperor often bestows a small pension on the widow. Most Omrah are thus adventurers, often of low descent, from different Mohammedan nations; within the empire they were raised by the emperor to the rank of dignitaries, or degraded into obscurity, according to his pleasure and caprice.

Uncertain about how long they will remain rich and without an incentive to save and pass on their wealth to their children, the Omrah sport the most extravagant lifestyles that are the ultimate in luxury and pomp. They live in grand mansions, surrounded by wives, concubines, slaves and dancing girls. They are waited upon by an army of servants, to the extent that at least two attendants are appointed for each of their horses and an elephant may have as many as four servants exclusively devoted to its upkeep. I knew an Amir who had three hundred torch-bearers in his service!

In keeping with their desired lifestyles, the Omrah dress in clothes of the finest silk and brocade and wear turbans woven with silver and gold thread. Their feet are clad in velvet sandals, the instep set with rubies and diamonds. Their women wear expensive jewellery made by the country's most gifted craftsmen. They are daily served with hundreds of rich dishes from their kitchens, and spend as recklessly on family celebrations as on games of chance. No Amir ever thinks of saving money but finds ever-new ways of spending it. Dost Khan, a swarthy Amir of Turkish origin concealed an essential frivolity behind a regal appearance and who called himself Danishmand Khan's friend (although I know the Agha did not think of him in the same way) once boasted to me of his new extravagance. Everyone knows how dear and scarce the essence of roses is. Yet neither scarcity nor high cost deterred Dost Khan from having his favourite horses rubbed with rosewater every day. Not to be outdone, his elder brother Mushtaq Khan, who was in charge of the emperor's treasury, was said to be building the most luxurious mansion the country had ever seen; it had everything except wings!

If there is a hint of censure in my description, a scorn of the lifestyle of Indian nobility, then I hasten to assure you that my disapproval does not spring from the base emotion of envy but from the moral outrage of a Christian upbringing that erupts through the philosophical neutrality M. Gassendi was at such pains to cultivate in my sensibility. Moral outrage results from moral blindness, my mentor often remarked. You must develop a capacity to look at both sides of an issue, he said, no matter how abhorrent you may feel about what you readily see. Remember, there are always aspects of the unseen that are not so obvious and will mitigate the initial moral outrage. So I shall also add that the Omrah are generous to a fault, even if this generosity is more impulsive than part of a well-considered design for leading a moral life. They are also warm-hearted, loyal to friends and exceptionally kind to strangers to whom they easily open their homes and hearts. I know, since I was one of those strangers.

'REMEMBER NICCOLAO, FIRST IMPRESSIONS are decisive. Especially with the Moguls, who attach great importance to the way they are approached.' Father Malpica's voice echoed in my ear as he helped me into the blue satin *qaba* that I had received as a gift, together with a handsome reward of ten rupees, from Wazir Khan the day after his wife had fully recovered.

I was due at Prince Dara's residence a little after sundown. A thunderstorm in the afternoon had markedly lowered the temperature and the Jesuit fathers had coaxed me into being finely clad for my interview with the Wali Ahad. I had given in after some initial resistance, being reassured that the weather now being what it was I would not be perspiring under the arms in the heavy satin garment and thus not emitting the smell peculiar to Europeans that Indians find offensive.

The fathers bantered continually as they busied themselves in preparing me for the evening.

'The way to earn the prince's favour is to display a passion for religion—not for the practices of various faiths but for what the prince believes is the unity that underlies them all,' said Father Buze, the plump Flemish priest who wore a full Mogul beard and counted himself among the Wali Ahad's friends.

Father Roth, lean, dark-haired and hollow-cheeked, was more cynical. 'Yes, it is only in discussions on religion that the prince permits dissent.'

'No, no!' cried Father Buze, suddenly defensive. 'You will not encounter a more open and liberal mind in all the courts of Europe. Before you accuse him of anything you must read the most recent of his writings, the *Majma-ul-Baharain*, "The Mingling of Two Oceans". I have a copy in my room.'

Curious, but not wanting to expose my deficient reading skills, I asked Father Buze what he thought of the book.

'It is a wonderful work. Any scholar will be proud to be identified as its author. The Prince has tried to cull together elements of the theory of Creation which are common to both Islamic and Hindu beliefs. His conclusion is that there is no difference between Hindus and Muslims in the ways of knowing God. The difference is in the language, in the words and expression, and not in the essence.'

'And see how he is reviled by the mullahs who rightly see in this book another step in the prince's turning away from what they regard as the true faith?' Father Roth countered. 'He may loftily term the outcry as the ranting of "ignorant blockheads" or be as dismissive of the ire of Believers as he is oblivious to the threat his brothers pose for him. The prince is rowing in very dangerous waters indeed.'

'Father, he is writing for the elect, not for the masses. We Jesuits should be the first to sympathize with that intention,' Father Buze said, stroking his beard with his right palm. 'The Wali Ahad rightly believes that he will be successful in convincing the elect of the two communities of his ideals, that he will bring Hindus and Muslims together and achieve his desire of mingling the two oceans. What nobility of thought! What lofty aspiration of brotherhood!'

I heard Father Roth snort softly while Father Malpica, ever a practical peacemaker, reached for a flagon of their favourite wine.

'Courtesy of the Wali Ahad,' Father Buze whispered severely in my ear.

My final lesson for the afternoon was the special salaam with which one pays obeisance to royalty. 'Stand erect, then bend your body forward until your forehead is close to the ground,' Father Malpica instructed. 'Place your right hand on the ground, the palm facing upwards, then raise it to your forehead and stand up straight. Repeat this three times although this is normally done only when approaching the emperor. But since you are a *farangi*, I am sure the prince will excuse the lapse.'

I did not miss the exchange of smiles and winks among the fathers as they watched my performance.

I was so dazed with excitement that I have few recollections of my first visit to Prince Dara's palace. Yet the ones that made their home in my memory are of surprising clarity.

Unlike in Venice, where the long afternoons slowly die in the golden light of the canals, in India the transition from daylight to darkness is swift. Night quickly swallowed the remnants of light from a rapidly sinking sun as I was escorted through a large garden. The mild, sweet scent of Molushri trees pervaded the air. Oil lamps were being lit, the smaller ones already twinkling in the bushes and on trees. The entrance to the palace apartments was guarded by two sentries and lit by torches on either side. Immediately inside the heavy, carved teak door studded with silver knobs was a lotus fountain, the radial petals at its outer circumference sculpted directly out of the white marble floor. Engravings inset with precious stones made the jets of water glitter in brilliant hues.

In the ante-chamber, where I waited for my summons, stood a casket with mother-of-pearl inlays. The pieces of shell, in lustrous pink and turquoise, gleamed against the dark rosewood base. I was anxious, yes, but my nervousness did not distract me from appreciating the beauty of the room. Panels in coloured mosaic depicting hunting scenes or combat between elephants lined the polished alabaster walls. Arched niches within the walls covered with panels of lotuses and leaves were inset with tiny mirrors, producing myriad reflecting surfaces. Prince Dara, I discovered later, shared the aesthetic leanings of Hindu princes in his penchant for floral motifs rather than the geometric patterns, arabesques and calligraphy favoured by the Mogul nobility. In his preference for the depiction of the Indian lotus rather than the central Asian poppy as the centrepiece of this decorative pattern he deviated even further from the artistic tastes of his ancestors.

The room into which I was finally led to meet the prince was the one where Prince Dara held his evening soirées. It was brightly lit by a huge chandelier of the finest Venetian crystal, delicately etched. Light cotton spreads decorated with floral motifs of scrolling vines and blossoms covered the white marble floor. About a dozen men lounged on these spreads, leaning against round bolsters covered in scarlet velvet embroidered with flowers and stalks in gold and silk threads.

My knees felt as though they would give way under me as I approached the platform where the Wali Ahad sat, holding court. Sweat poured down my face, and just as I felt it was a huge mistake to have ever left the comforting safety of the Jesuits' house, the familiar sight of Father Buze's bearded face smiling encouragingly at me slowed down the beating of my heart. Taking a deep breath, I bowed low to greet the prince, just as the fathers had taught me.

The prince appeared delighted to see that a youth, a *farangi* at that, not only spoke Persian but had learnt how to pay proper obeisance to a royal. He asked me a few questions about Venice, to which I gave truthful answers, and a couple on my medical background, to which I did not. When he asked me about my origins, I did not pretend that I was of noble lineage although I did lie in telling him I was a *cittadini originarii*, among those citizens who have a high status in Venetian society because they belong to the corps of scribes and notaries.

'Ah, like the Brahmins among the Hindus,' the prince remarked, and wanted to know more about what he called 'your caste system'.

'Not exactly like Brahmins, Your Highness,' I said. '*Cittadini originarii* may also be traders. It is just that they must be descendants of two generations of Venetian citizens and neither they nor their fathers should have exercised a mechanical occupation.'

The prince nodded in understanding, took a long drag from his hukka, the water in the bowl of green glass with lotus flowers etched in gold gurgling loudly like an old man clearing his throat of morning catarrh. He asked me with a smile, 'Would you like to enter my service, *farangi*?'

I had waited for months with a ready answer to this question.

'I can hardly believe that I will have the good fortune to serve under so famous a prince,' I said, bowing low.

The prince turned to one of the dozen retainers standing against the walls—four carrying flagons of wine, others awaiting orders—and directed one of them to immediately give me a sum of thirty rupees, a complete set of vestments and a good horse. He also announced that I should be paid eighty rupees a month and that suitable quarters be hired for my accommodation.

Father Buze later told me that most of the men I had seen that day were Prince Dara's drinking companions. They were the elite among Delhi's liberal Muslim poets and scholars. The Sufi poet Sarmad, a fakir with conspicuously bushy eyebrows, wearing nothing more than a white loincloth, was present that evening. As was Halim, a man with the heavy face of a peasant, whom Father Malpica described as a scholar who had burst upon the literary scene with what was considered a majestic history of religions, the *Dabistan-i-Mazahib*. Also there that evening were the prince's chief scribe, Chandra Bhan, who allegedly indulged in a drinking binge at least once every month; the youthful Muhandis, who had assisted his father Ustad Isa Khan in the construction of the Taj Mahal; and, in a corner, sitting at some distance from the rest, drinking sherbet rather than wine and dressed in white cotton dhotis with muslin scarves thrown across their shoulders to cover their bare chests, were two scholars of the Hindu religion, both in their mid-thirties, who were initiating the Wali Ahad into the mysteries of their faith. I, Niccolao Manucci, who had grown up on the streets of Venice and had once scrounged for food in its dockyards, could never have imagined in my most audacious fantasies that I was to be a frequent visitor to this august court in the days to come.

Excitement plays tricks with memory. Although I can recollect the room and the objects in it in precise detail, I have little memory of the prince's face, stature or attire from that first visit. I remember a hand, its fingers covered with flashing rings, raising a goblet to his mouth. I remember the magnificent vessel encrusted with rubies and emeralds in the shapes of blossoms and leaves. I remember a turban glittering with strings of rubies and sapphires, a head thrown back in a sputtering laugh, and drops of red wine staining a lightly bearded jaw. I remember the impression the Wali Ahad left on me on that first meeting: a comely prince with a hearty laugh, whose generosity and warmth had quickly put me at ease.

Today, when people ask me about Prince Dara, I am able to provide a well-considered judgement based on years of observation and free of any misleading spontaneity of first impressions. The Wali Ahad, I tell them, was a man of dignified manners, exquisitely polite in conversation and quick at repartee. He was brilliant, straightforward, and endowed with courage and energy, both physical and mental. Whatever he did was performed with so much ease, his actions accompanied by so much grace that even the most disgruntled of men could not help but feel attracted to his person. If he had inherited his father's love of pomp and magnificence and a weakness for astrology, he had also inherited the emperor's munificence, his generous appreciation of learning and scholarship and a refined taste in music and painting. To me the greatest of his virtues was his innate kindness.

Those ill-inclined towards him have called it a soft-heartedness that was susceptible to flattery. That, I have always felt, is unjust. The prince never used his boundless influence with his father to injure any person, though he often misused it to benefit many unworthy people. Nothing pleased him more than the liberal exercise of royal clemency to spare a life, however justly forfeited. He never withheld it, even against rebels like Champat Rai Bundela, who proved to be the worst of ingrates. I have no doubt that in the end he even forgave that scoundrel Malik Jivan whose miserable life he saved twice, the last time when that betrayer was being readied for execution on the Police Prefect's platform in Delhi. Prince Dara did not carry grudges. If he was susceptible to outbursts of anger then they were seldom more than momentary. In my opinion, the prince's thunder was not half as menacing as that wretch Aurangzeb's faint smile.

My employment in Prince Dara's service was like the royal seal on the proclamation of my medical competence. My practice began to flourish as patients poured in. My attempt was to channel the stream from the very beginning.

'If you really want to make a reputation as a physician,' Vaidraj had told me, 'be a specialist.'

Maria assiduously helped me in this undertaking by spreading the word that I was a veritable Avicenna in the treatment of diseases that afflicted women. The curing of Wazir Khan's wife, now raised to the stature of a miracle, was still fresh in people's minds, with the result that many women in the harems of the nobles began to demand my services when they fell ill.

My early successes resulted from a mixture of luck and vigilance in selecting only healthy patients for treatment. By 'healthy' I mean women whose sickness was not life-threatening, who in time would have recovered on their own. I refused the very serious cases, pleading lack of time to give them the full attention they required. Miracles are miracles precisely because they cannot be predicted or willed. It would have been foolish of me to hope for another one.

The bread and butter of my practice came from bloodletting, in which I had gained proficiency. Many women routinely had themselves bled every month to expel the poisons in the bloodstream that could lead to such blemishes as pimples or even unsightly warts.

My first session of bloodletting, which took place in the harem of Rustam Khan, one of the Wali Ahad's favourite commanders, was unnerving to say the least. As the Aitmad led me into the harem and closed the door behind us, three or four old women rapidly approached me and conducted me to a bathroom. Ignoring my protests, they began to undress me, making lewd comments and cackling with mirth when I tried to cover my manhood with my hands. I had never had any cause to doubt that I was reasonably endowed, but this mockery made me feel like my genitals had reduced to the size of a small boy's. The women then washed me well, especially my hands, and anointed me with aromatic pomades. This was accompanied by some uncomfortably indiscreet groping and more laughter. After I was dressed in fresh clothes, I was escorted to the sick woman's bedside, the shawl thrown over my head now trailing down to my waist. From behind a curtain a slender arm was extended in my direction. The arm was fully covered till the wrist. I first felt the pulse, which was strong and steady, and indicated a spot the width of two fingers above the wrist, close to the vein that I wanted to bleed. One of the old women pushed up the silk cloth covering my patient's arm. Instead of making shallow incisions with a scalpel, which would have left faint scars on my fair patient's arm, I used the silver needle I had brought with me to prick the vein. Another woman handed me a gold basin to gather the blood and I examined it for colour before pricking another vein in the foot. This was not really necessary but I knew both the patient and the watching women expected that the bloodletting is repeated at least once, if not many more times, during a single session for it to be truly effective. Such sessions soon became routine and I even began to enjoy the ritual that led up to the procedure, laughing along with the old crones, sharing their glee as they undressed me and prepared my body for the bath.

As terrible as it may sound, the bulk of my practice came from the sorry situation of the women in the harem. In their jealousy, the Muslims were even worse than the Portuguese. They were exceedingly distrustful of their women and did not trust their wives, even with their own brothers. So strict, in fact, was the Muslim purdah that the helpless women had no choice but to adopt its values as their own. If a fire broke out in the harem, many women would prefer to perish in the flames than expose their faces to strange men while fleeing. One of the emperor's queens was said to observe purdah to such an extent that she refused to take a male child on her lap and covered her face even in the presence of a four-year-old boy. Amir Khan, the governor of Kabul, had gone so far as to divorce his wife because her veil got dislodged, exposing her face, when she attempted to save her life by leaping from the back of an elephant which was running amok.

Confined to the harem like caged birds and closely guarded by trusted eunuchs and female *daroghas*, the women pined for attention. In the inevitable absence of physical intimacy, they longed to touch and be touched by a man. Each day, they spent hours adorning themselves in clothes and jewellery and perfuming their bodies with unusual scents; not in the hope of a visit from their Lord, which is rare, but to fill the emptiness of their lives. There were diversions, of course, of gossip and intrigues, dance and musical recitals by the slave girls. Some of the talented women memorized stories—such favourites as tales from the popular tales, *Hazar Afsane* (*A Thousand Nights*)—as also whole verses from Persian romantic poetry, which they then related to an enthusiastic audience. Except for the royal princesses, the harem women were illiterate. The tales and the verses had been transmitted orally from older women to those in the younger generation who were blessed both by a good memory and a voice that brought out the subtleties of the prose and the music of the verse.

Yet the minds of most women remained home to salacious thoughts and their bodies to unfulfilled urges. Liaisons with other women, or even with eunuchs, though not uncommon, attracted harsh punishments. All that remained for a woman was the possibility of pleasuring herself, sometimes through unusual means, but this too was sought to be interdicted. The eunuchs were under strict instructions to ensure that any fruit or vegetable that was shaped like the *membrum virile*—a radish or cucumber and especially the long brinjal with its purple satiny skin—was cut, and jaggedly so, before it was allowed into the harem's kitchen.

Under the circumstances, visits from a young doctor resulted in much excitement and anticipation. Quite a few of the women pretended to be invalid, simply to have a chance to converse with me and have their pulse felt by me. Not that it is easy to find the pulse on a wrist covered with bracelets or strings of pearls wrapped around it ten or twelve times. On occasion, when I stretched my hand to reach inside the curtain to feel the pulse of a woman who pretended to be too weak to extend her arm outside, I felt it being kissed by soft lips or the flesh under my thumb nibbled at by small, sharp teeth. The bolder among the women, either in collusion with the *darogha* on duty or evading her watchful gaze, rubbed their cheeks against my palm or lewdly placed the swell of a naked breast against it. I was young, full of the sap of youth, and had to exercise strong self-control not to respond to the touch. That would have been hazardous to my plans, not to speak of being fatal for my person. I could not help the involuntary reactions of my body, however. Whenever I went to see a patient in a harem, I was careful to wear a *qaba* that came down to my knees and trousers that flapped loosely around the hips.

My monthly salary in the prince's employment was generous but I needed to supplement it as my expenses were high. Even the horse the Wali Ahad had gifted me was a financial burden since I did not know how to ride a horse and was nervous around the animal. That is, till the man I employed to take care of the animal suggested that I hire it out to people who were visiting the city on business and wanted to make an impression by arriving for their appointments on a horse instead of on foot.

Eight days later, another opportunity to make easy money presented itself. One morning, just after the scavenger who came with his donkey to remove the garbage had made his rounds, a man came to my house and asked if I was interested in making some money without working for it. What exactly did he mean, I enquired. He said all he needed was my permission to distil spirits close to my house and under my protection, and for me to assert that he was my servant. Drinking alcohol is forbidden in both the religions, Hindu and Muslim, though this does not prevent common people from clandestinely drinking a liquor called arak locally distilled from molasses. Its consumption and sale are strictly forbidden, but widespread corruption in the police force ensures its easy availability. Europeans in the service of Prince Dara had the privilege of distilling spirits and selling them without hindrance. The Jesuit fathers, who did not have the financial support of the Church and had to fall back on their own resources, had also adopted this as their chief source of income. Arak is even offered in some taverns in a disguised form once it has been mixed with coloured sherbets. In spite of the religious prohibition, some nobles openly drink Shiraz wine imported from Persia, while others are partial to the Canary wine brought into Surat by the Dutch. Both wines are so dear that, as they say in Venice, the taste is destroyed by the cost.

The man, a ruffian by his looks, offered me a fee of ten rupees a day for my service. A little haggling enabled me to get the man to raise my share to twelve rupees and I agreed to his proposal. Growing up poor, I had always been careful about money and did not disdain these petty sources of income even after I had established myself as a physician at the court.

As far as alternative sources of income were concerned, the Mogul court itself was a goldmine; all a man needed to extract the gold was enough enterprise to explore its depths. In this I found Maria to be the perfect partner. She was resourceful, knowledgeable about the nature of Indians and, to my delight, mischievously inventive in her scheming. Soon after I began my practice in earnest, she revealed to me that the only time a resident of a harem was allowed to come face to face with a man was when she was thought to be possessed by a spirit. On such occasions, an exorcist was called upon to observe her physical condition and monitor the progress of the spirit's expulsion. Such cases, in fact, occurred frequently and the guardians of the harem ensured that the exorcist who was summoned was a geriatric. (It had not escaped my notice that possession of women by demons occurred more often in places where women were confined and had little interaction with the opposite gender; nunneries in my country and harems in India were preferred sites for demonic visitations.) It was time, Maria declared, for me to develop another skill, a specialization within a specialization, so to speak. She had a perfect plan by which I could establish a reputation as an exorcist.

One evening, I invited a small group from among the Omrah at the prince's court to my house for dinner. Those who accepted the invitation did not belong to the highest echelons of the court and I must admit I was relieved as the dinner I was serving would have been quite poor by Mogul standards. In a Mogul feast, serving anything less than forty dishes is considered dishonourable of the host and insulting to the guests—though ignorance of etiquette is excusable in a *farangi*.

After dinner, we were sitting around companionably smoking hukkas and drinking Shiraz wine when, in the middle of a conversation, I turned to address a corner of the room as though speaking to an invisible entity.

'Quiet!' I called out. 'Can't you see I am busy with my guests? Hold your tongue!'

I resumed talking to the nobles as if nothing had happened, but occasionally pretended to cast irritated glances at the same empty corner. The nobles exchanged alarmed looks. Then, suddenly, as one of them began to address me, I cut him off with a raised hand and began to shout at the corner.

'Did I not command you to shut up? Quiet, I say!'

I repeated this performance three times in the next hour, pretending each time to be more provoked than before, yet I continued to smile at my guests and offer them more wine as if nothing untoward was taking place. All conversation had now ceased. Finally, I rose from my seat in great anger and advanced towards the window, uttering the choicest abuses. On the way, I took a bottle from the table (into which Maria had sneakily poured a little arak) and lit it with a candle. As the bottle glowed blue with flames, I opened the window and violently hurled it out, abusing the invisible demon some more and forbidding him to enter my home ever again. The petrified Omrah, now visibly shaken, could not wait to get away but were too scared to walk the small distance between my house and their waiting carriages. I reassured them that the demon was safely in my power and to keep him at bay all they had to do was to repeat '*Farangi hakim ki duhai! Farangi hakim ki duhai!*' ('I call upon the protection of the *farangi* doctor!').

And so, in addition to being a respected physician, I gained the reputation of being an expert exorcist. For the purpose of healing, whether it is of body or spirit, reputation is all, and I worked hard at improving mine. The native exorcists used talismans containing appropriate Quranic verses and the names of Allah—Al-Muhyi, Al-Qadri, Al-Hefiz—written by a calligrapher to repulse spirit attacks. Depending on the nature of the possessing spirit, the talisman was employed in various ways. It could be tied around the patient's neck or around an arm. It could be burnt and the patient fumigated with its smoke. Its writing could be dissolved in water, which was then consumed by the patient. It could be wrapped in a piece of cotton soaked in perfumed oil and then burnt as the wick of a lamp at her bedside. The method I employed to expel spirits possessing the bodies of women was more dramatic. I conducted evil-smelling fumigations, beat drums and rung a bell; I shouted, threw my arms around, leapt up and down and, on occasion, even recited the 'Hail Mary' in rapid-fire Italian. It was a performance I thoroughly enjoyed as, I suspect, did some of the possessed women, even when I used a cane to administer a light beating —confining the blows to the woman's buttocks and thighs, of course.

I had another trump up my sleeve but resisted letting Maria in on the secret for the longest time—perhaps because its very purpose demanded utmost secrecy, or perhaps because I was unsure whether it really worked. This was Vaidraj's recipe for the ointment that would ensure a man's sexual fealty. Its prescription had to be limited to only one woman per harem since any hint that I was favouring one wife or concubine over others would have aroused so much jealousy among them and ire towards me that my practice would have been jeopardized. More than that, unlike other medical treatments, the failure of the treatment could not be easily explained away by the doctor since its effects would not manifest themselves in the patient but in her husband, whom the doctor would never meet.

Maria was thrilled when she heard about it.

'Why didn't you tell me about this earlier, Nicco?' she said, breathless with excitement. 'If the ointment works, it will be as if you have been given the key to the treasure chests of the Omrah with an invitation to help yourself to their contents. You cannot imagine the demand it will have in the harems. I understand we have to limit its supply, but that is even better because reducing the supply will further increase its price. If the ointment does not work, a woman will be too ashamed to let it be known that she used it. As for your other apprehension, there is a simple solution. We will become partners and I will distribute the ointment. If anybody should ask, I will say that I obtained the recipe from a most learned Hindu doctor; your name need never be mentioned.'

I let myself be convinced, by Maria as much as by my own greed. For a few months we carried on a discreet but hugely profitable business in dispensing the ointment to carefully selected women in different harems. The large chest I kept under my bed soon began to bulge with gold coins and chains, strings of pearl, gold rings and armlets encrusted with precious gems, which grateful clients had gifted to Maria. How were we to know that the consequences of our avarice would soon be upon us?

Given the circumstances of our lives, it was inevitable that Maria and I would become lovers. Wary about preserving my reputation at this time, I was careful not to visit prostitutes as I had during my carefree days in Goa. The prince's *wazir* frequently made offers of the services of slave girls, but I refused him every time. On Maria's advice, I had set out to create the image of a celibate doctor, as much a priest as a physician. The ladies of the harem, Maria had told me, found this combination both reassuring and intriguing and I had already become the subject of much gossip, salacious as well as reverential. 'A doctor cannot ask for anything better,' she had reassured. But I was not just a doctor; I was also very much a man of flesh and blood and all the consequent needs. Maria, too, possessed a certain restlessness, that of a woman who has been deprived of physical love for a long time. However influential her position in the harem, she was still a slave (though one with some freedom of movement), and had been starved of intimacy with a man ever since she was separated from her husband after the fall of Hoogly. Every Sunday, under the pretext of carrying out her religious observances with the Jesuit fathers and unobserved by her escorts, who waited outside, she would slip out of the back door and into my house through the wicker gate in the compound wall that separated the two properties. The fathers were worldly men and, other than Father Roth who initially voiced mild protests, they indulgently tolerated the arrangement.

What began as an agreement of convenience soon developed into a passionate affair. On those Sunday afternoons, lying entwined in bed aware of their impending separation, our bodies could not have enough of each other. Maria not only matched my ardour but fuelled it to a point where the keenness of pleasure keels into pain. Spent, we never alluded to the sublime love our bodies had just shared. Instead we discussed the happenings at the Wali Ahad's court, the gossip in the harem, our business arrangements, even as our bodies and souls quietly glowed in the aftermath of exquisite pleasure. If Maria developed feelings of a more tender kind for me than what our arrangement strictly required, she never revealed them. And if she did, then I, in the single-minded pursuit of my goal, hardly took notice. As with Mala, I repaid Maria's generosity not with unkindness but with worse—a benevolent indifference.

I should have known that partnerships begun in bed should remain confined to the bed. Extending them to business proves inevitably disastrous, both for business and for the bed.

WITHIN TWO MONTHS OF my entering the service of Danishmand Khan, and even though I was a foreigner only recently arrived in the Indies, I sensed the singular unease that was rippling through the empire like a wave in the bowels of the ocean.

My close observation of the lives and more of the Omrah did not blind me to the happenings at the Mogul court, and from my close interrogation of the Agha's head eunuch, Khwaja Chisti, of whose peculiar situation I will speak later, I understood that the peace of the empire was threatened by a looming crisis. The nature of the crisis can only be understood if I first give a brief historical background. Just as we can better appreciate the present condition of a person if we are also conversant with his past, the contemporary circumstances of a country reveals deeper patterns if we are aware of its history.

Since the Moguls lack our principle of primogeniture wherein the eldest son takes the place of his departed father, the succession to the throne of India has always been contentious and is decided upon by the strength of arms. Bloody wars between brothers, or even between father and son, have been the rule rather than the exception in the House of Timur. The present emperor Shah Jahan's grandfather, Humayun, was perhaps the kindest in that he exiled one of his brothers and blinded the other after emerging victorious in the war of succession. Emperor Shah Jahan himself had rebelled against *his* father and marked his accession to the throne by murdering his brothers and nephews. It is entirely lawful for the great sovereigns, say the mullahs, the interpreters of Mohammedan law, to rid the mortal world of their brothers and other relations whose annihilation is conducive to the common good.

To be a Mogul prince is, therefore, to grow up carrying the disturbing knowledge that your destined end is either to be raised to glory and power far surpassing that of any European monarch, or to die by slow-poisoning or a quicker thrust of the dagger at the hands of your brother. Deep in the heart of a prince, there can thus be little room for brotherly sentiment or, indeed, filial piety; the fate of fathers and sons, and of brothers, is dominated by rivalry and images of violent death rather than by loyalty and memories of affectionate embraces.

As Emperor Shah Jahan aged, he had increasingly come to be haunted by violent imaginings from his own past and his ancestral history. Tormented by the forebodings of the events that had their origins in his memories, and in perpetual apprehension of his sons taking recourse to arms as he had once done against his own father, the monarch had sought to save himself from impending calamity and guarantee his safety by bestowing upon his sons the government of four distant provinces. His eldest son Dara Shukoh was appointed the governor of Kabul and Multan; the second son Sultan Shuja, of Bengal; the third son Aurangzeb, of the Deccan; and the youngest, Murad Baksh, of Gujarat. With the exception of Dara Shukoh, who selected a governor to look after his assigned provinces, the other princes reluctantly repaired to their far-off domains where they acted as independent sovereigns and appropriated the revenues of the province to raise formidable armies for the war of succession that had begun to loom large on the horizon.

Dara Shukoh had stayed back in Delhi, not only because the emperor liked him the best—love would be too strong a word to characterize relations between a Mogul father and son—but also because the monarch had to ensure that at least one son was bound to him to secure his own survival. When I entered Danishmand Khan's service, I soon gathered that the Omrah knew that the emperor wanted wanted his elder son to be his successor. This indication of their sovereign's wishes did not, however, stop them from secretly dividing into factions, each supporting the claim of one or the other prince.

Such division among the nobles is not a matter of mere court intrigue, without relevance to the lives of the common people. With the emperor exercising absolute power far greater than that of a European king, no business can be done at the court, whether it is a European ambassador seeking permission to set up a trading factory or a poor scholar praying to be granted a few acres of rent-free land, without the help of a patron who intercedes with the emperor on behalf of the supplicant. The closer a noble is perceived to be to the emperor, the greater his prestige as a patron. For his trouble, a patron is recompensed with what Indians, in their love for circumlocution, call 'presents', rather than the bribes they actually are. The disquiet was thus not limited to the court but spread through the empire as the patrons—with their retinues of feudatories in dispute with their neighbours, contiguous vassal states quarrelling over their boundaries and even foreign trading companies bent on elbowing out one another—scrambled to forge alliances and form factions allied to one or the other prince. The largest faction was in support of Dara, the Wali Ahad, followed by one which espoused the cause of Aurangzeb, and smaller ones of Shuja and Murad.

Dara's cause as the Wali Ahad was greatly aided by the affection his sister Jahanara Begum held for him. They also shared common spiritual interests and were the followers of a Sufi fakir, one of the many eccentric, if not half-mad, religious zealots that abound in the Indies, both among the Mohammedans and the idolaters.

When he spoke of the exploits of the royal princesses, Khwaja Chisti always lowered his voice to a conspiratorial whisper that nevertheless did not conceal a malicious glee. After the death of his beloved wife, Mumtaz Mahal, Jahanara was the only person the ageing emperor completely trusted and, indeed, passionately loved. In his fear of being poisoned by one of his sons, Emperor Shah Jahan had even entrusted the preparation of his food to his favourite daughter. The princess was reputed to be a beautiful woman, faultless of feature and form. When I was at the court I found it to be common knowledge that the monarch's love for his daughter had crossed into the darker realms of incest. One of the highest-ranking mullahs at the court even justified the emperor's proclivity by observing that it would be unjust to deny the king the privilege of gathering fruit from the tree he himself had planted.

Jahanara Begum, who had the normal appetites of a healthy young woman, was compelled to take lovers and entertain them secretly in the seraglio, an enterprise that was attended by grave peril. It was inevitable that jealousy stemming from possessiveness would follow in the wake of the emperor's perverted passion for his daughter. In spite of Dara's pleas on behalf of his sister, Emperor Shah Jahan had reportedly been adamant in his refusal to allow her to marry Najabat Khan, a general in the imperial army who was a descendant of the royal house of Balkh. In fact, one of the chief reasons for her embracing Dara's cause with such enthusiasm was his promise that he would grant her permission to marry on his accession to the throne.

Except for his disapproval of her affairs of the heart, or rather, the body, the emperor could refuse nothing to Jahanara. She, in turn, doted on her eldest brother and helped him procure unimaginable favours from their father. Dara sat on a sofa beneath the imperial throne, the only instance of a Mogul prince being allowed to be seated in the presence of the emperor. He could issue orders to the officials of the state and had the privilege of commanding a combat of elephants whenever he wished, a distinction otherwise reserved for the sovereign alone. It was thus a natural human reaction that the younger sister Roshanara Begum, neither blessed with the beauty and sunny disposition of her elder sister, nor included in the love feasts between father and daughter or between eldest brother and sister, turned to her younger brother, Aurangzeb. She became an indispensable ally to the younger prince, supplying him with highly useful intelligence on what was happening at the court and advising him on how to take advantage of the shifting coalitions and alliances. Not to be left out of the web of intrigue being woven at the court, Gauhanara Begum, the emperor's youngest daughter, became an ally of the second son, Shah Shuja.

With the emperor beginning to keep indifferent health, the crisis seemed to be coming to a head and it was the fate of the empire that was responsible for the preoccupied mien of Danishmand Khan, which I encountered every morning when I presented myself at his court. In his outward behaviour he remained as courteous as ever, but there was no disguising the fact that he was in a hurry to get away to more important meetings with a few trusted friends with whom he could share his concerns.

One such friend and a welcome visitor to the Agha's mansion was Jafar Khan, the minister in charge of the imperial treasury and a relation of the emperor's as he was married to Mumtaz Mahal's sister. Both men saw themselves as servants of the House of Timur, dedicated to safeguarding the interests of the empire; both were worried about the growing political uncertainty in the kingdom as a consequence of the emperor's ailing health and his virtual withdrawal from the affairs of state. Given the sensitive nature of their discussions, they took care to hold their meetings in the pavilion in the garden with only the head eunuch of the Agha's harem, Khwaja Chisti, being allowed to approach them to serve refreshments. If someone like me, a *farangi* and recent entrant in the service of Danishmand Khan, became privy to these discussions, then it was solely because the same Khwaja Chisti befriended me soon after I arrived in Delhi.

A dignified man in his early forties, plump of figure and round of face, but with the smooth skin of a ten-year-old boy, Khwaja Chisti had one day accosted me on my way out of the mansion with a most unusual request. Contrary to what every man in India yearns for, namely the enhancement of his sexual potency, Khwaja Chisti wanted to know whether there was any remedy in *farangi* medicine which eliminates sexual desire altogether. He had fallen passionately in love with a slave girl, demonstrating the fallacy of an opinion entertained by myself as well as by others that he who is entirely deprived of manhood cannot feel the urges of passion. Khwaja Chisti confessed that he had frequent and intense sexual feelings and even ejaculated some mucous in the throes of voluptuous sensations engendered by dreams of the girl caressing his penis and scrotum, both of which had been removed when he was thirteen. He could not bear the indignity of these nocturnal occurrences and I promised him I would consult my medical books to find a cure.

To show his appreciation for my goodwill and to satisfy my natural curiosity on what was happening at the court, Khwaja Chisti began to share with me the substance of every conversation between the two ministers within hours of their meetings. He claimed he was repeating some of it verbatim, mimicking with considerable pleasure the measured cadences of the Agha's speech as also the more clipped delivery of Jafar Khan, although I had no way of judging the veracity of this particular claim or, indeed, the accuracy of his reports of what transpired in the course of their confabulations. From what the eunuch told me, I gathered that Jafar Khan was trying to persuade the Agha to take a more active stance in support of Prince Aurangzeb, whose cause he had made his own. Having closely observed the political developments in the land since my arrival, I understood well that 'active', in the current circumstance, did not mean 'open'; a forthright declaration of support for Aurangzeb as successor to the throne of India would amount to treason and invite the wrath of both the emperor and the crown prince. Jafar Khan wanted only that Danishmand Khan's preference be known more widely among the Omrah so it may help tip those who were still hesitant into Aurangzeb's camp.

The two ministers agreed that it would be a calamity for the House of Timur if either of the other princes, Sultan Shuja or Murad

Baksh, were to ascend the throne. Sultan Shuja, the second son, was intelligent, discreet, firm of purpose—but only when he was sober. A slave to his pleasures, once he was surrounded by his women, who exceeded a rational number, he spent whole days and nights dancing, singing and drinking wine. However, his greater drawback, Chisti said, was that he had declared himself a follower of the Shia heresy, the religion of the Persians that was anathema to a pious and orthodox Sunni like Jafar Khan, a kind and tolerant man except in matters of faith, for whom a Shia on the throne of India would be a calamity he could not countenance.

The objections of our Agha, who too was a Sunni but far less conservative than Jafar Khan in the interpretation of his faith, were more professional than personal, and stemmed from his position as the foreign minister of the empire. For two hundred years, the cornerstone of Mogul foreign policy had been to counter the threat to the empire by the heretical Persians. For over a century the two countries had intermittently gone to war over the northern province of Kandahar, which had often changed hands. One of the reasons why the recently failed expedition of the Mogul army to capture the fort of Kandahar had not excited passionate comment at the court or in the bazaars was that such reverses were as much part of the long-drawn-out struggle against Persia as were the occasional successes. Danishmand Khan had laboured hard on the traditional strategy of isolating Persia by building a coalition with the Sunni rulers of Turkey and Balkh and the Uzbek rulers of Transoxonia. Indeed, he was expecting an Uzbek embassy the very next week and had graciously invited me to be present at the dinner he was hosting for them. Sultan Shuja's ascent to the throne would throw a tried-and-tested foreign policy into utter disarray.

The youngest son, Murad Baksh, was generous, polite and excelled the other brothers in bodily strength and sheer animal courage. '*Azman kase bahadur nis* (There is none braver than I),' he often bragged. Like all Mogul princes—except Aurangzeb—he was pleasure-loving, but was addicted solely to food. His breakfast alone consisted of trotters of a kid goat cooked with a little turmeric, onions and whole black peppers on a slow fire through the night, a leg of lamb marinated with a mixture of coriander, cardamom, cloves and cashewnut paste and grilled in a clay oven, together with platters of six different kinds of kebabs served in massive silver tureens with ornate gold handles. His father once remarked of him that Murad cared only for the nourishment of his body, that he was a *tanparwar*. His fatal flaw was a singular lack of judgement, an essential prerequisite for a ruler. All other failings of a monarch are not so grave that they cannot be compensated for by a judicious selection of counsellors who can provide the subjects and the realm with what the ruler himself lacks. Deficient judgement with regard to one's own abilities and those of other men is a certain recipe for failure and it was no surprise that Murad had hitherto failed in every task the emperor had entrusted to him.

Where the two ministers differed, less in substance than in the strength of their feelings, was in their appraisal of Dara Shukoh. Jafar Khan, normally courteous to the core, could scarcely hide his aversion to the crown prince, while the Agha never hid his fondness for the prince even when he disapproved of him.

'Ah, my friend, I agree with you. Dara can be inordinately insulting when he loses his temper,' Khwaja Chisti reported the Agha as telling Jafar Khan. 'I do not mind his boorishness towards me. Irascibility in a ruler is a deplorable trait that causes but little harm. Sometimes it may even be useful in preventing inappropriate familiarity and in instilling much-needed fear.'

Although I had been in Delhi for less than a couple of months I, too, had heard stories about Dara Shukoh's lack of tact in dealing with the Mogul nobility who attach much importance to what they call *izzat* or personal honour. A slight on their honour normally invites lethal retribution, but the Omrah were helpless when the source of the affront was a member of the royal family. Nothing held Dara back from publicly insulting many of the Omrah and he had even slighted Prime Minister Sadullah Khan on more than one occasion, requiring the emperor's intervention to soothe the injured *amour-propre* of a man the emperor esteemed as an able administrator and valuable adviser.

'No doubt the Wali Ahad possesses the resources, majesty and pomp of a king,' Shah Jahan had written to his favourite son after one such instance when Dara had accused Sadullah Khan of cheating him out of some land revenue, 'but he appears to be inimical to honest people. The Wali Ahad is good to bad men and bad to the good ones.'

Khwaja Chisti reported another conversation where Jafar Khan's normally clipped speech had occasionally degenerated into sputters of outrage.

'What I dread with his ascension to the throne is much worse than bad manners: I fear the disappearance of Islam from Hindustan!' Jafar Khan had said, adjusting his turban that had come askew in his excitement. 'You see how he surrounds himself with infidels and takes great pleasure in translating their religious books. He openly professes allegiance to the Sufi heresy that all religions have the same goal, only the paths are different. He claims that he is an *arif* who has known and glimpsed the unveiled face of God and thus no longer needs to comply with the injunctions of the Sharia. I hear that in his own court he openly repeats the Sufi heresy of that shameless Mullah Shah that a true Believer is the infidel who has attained God and an infidel is a Believer who has not seen or known Him. And he has even had the effrontery to write, "Life lies concealed in every idol and Faith lies hidden behind Infidelity".'

'Ah, Jafar, my friend, you exaggerate,' the Agha had countered, 'Prince Dara remains a Believer. There are no indications that he has renounced Prophet Mohammed, *sallallahou alayhi wasallam*, peace be upon him.'

'I grant you that he has yet to outdo his great-grandfather, Emperor Akbar, who made scandalous remarks about the moral character of the Prophet. Emperor Akbar simply pushed the Prophet aside, disobeyed Allah's command that Mohammed was the last of the prophets and even aspired to form an Ummat of his own. But give Dara Shukoh a few years on the throne and I dread the consequence for the religion of Mohammed and the rule of the Mughals. I hear he wears a ring inscribed in the script of the infidels, and it says "Prabhu", one of the names the wretched infidels have for their God, or is it one of their many gods, I never know which.'

'You are right about the danger to the empire if the Wali Ahad ascends the throne,' said Danishmand Khan. 'I wish Prince Dara's pursuits were less intellectual and his aims less spiritual. How different he would have been if he had studied less philosophy and more military science, if he had devoted to administration the time he has spent in writing books. If the Wali Ahad had more worldly cunning in him and less mystic spiritualism I would have bowed to my emperor's choice and never entertained disloyal thoughts.'

Danishmand Khan had supervised the education of the princes when they were children but, and this is one of the many qualities I admired in him, he did not let his personal liking for his former charge come in the way of a fair and objective assessment of the eldest prince's character.

'I remember that even when he was studying Persian poetry, Prince Dara showed far less interest in the epics of Firdausi and Sadi than in the mystical verse of Rumi and Jami. The miracles performed by saints spoke to him more than the exploits of warrior heroes. His later association with Sufi and Hindu mystics has developed in him a frame of mind that is credulous, sensitive and impractical. And that is the danger, my friend. Once you begin to lose contact with the real world and dwell more and more in your own mind, your judgement will be warped no matter how brilliant your mind is. Dara believes whatever he wishes, and whatever he believes he sees in dreams and visions and not in the world as it is. He is convinced that he can accomplish everything by the powers of his mind. What frightens me is that he considers himself competent in all matters and does not feel the need to consult advisers, as if knowledge of the Divine, which he claims to possess, also gives him knowledge of state finances or of warfare. No one has a higher opinion of the ability of the Wali Ahad than the prince himself. Do you know that he even lets himself be addressed as *al-kamil*, the perfect man?'

'Why do you then hesitate to join Aurangzeb's party?' Jafar Khan asked. 'He will be a great monarch, perhaps the greatest in the Timur dynasty. I have interacted closely with the prince during our campaign against the Persians. I have seen with my own eyes that he is a shrewd judge of human character. He has an indefatigable capacity for work, even routine work which seems to tire the Wali Ahad so quickly. Aurangzeb is the only prince, perhaps in the history of the House of Timur, who spurns luxury and the pleasures of the senses. Above all, he is a pious and God-fearing Muslim who carries out the injunctions of the Sharia exactly as prescribed, without deviating from it an iota in letter or spirit. He will restore Islam in India to its pristine glory, my friend. He will clean its holy river from the polluting streams of laxity and heresy that have been flowing into it ever since the time of Emperor Akbar.'

'You will not find me hesitating when the time comes to do my duty,' Danishmand Khan replied.

'Ah, our Agha is a canny one, Bernier,' Khwaja Chisti said with glee, tapping his temple with a forefinger. 'Jafar Khan had to content himself with this enigmatic response.'

I know I have been accused of being biased against Dara, the heir apparent, especially by the Europeans in his service, but anyone who has read *Lataif-ul-akhbar*, a detailed account of Dara's siege of Kandahar, a book that was widely circulated when I was in Delhi, cannot but give assent to Jafar Khan's charges.

Take the matter of Dara's credulity. I am well aware that Indians, and indeed all orientals, are excessively superstitious and consult astrologers for almost every occasion of import, but the prince's dependence on people who would dictate an auspicious time for an army to march, begin a siege or launch an assault I found well beyond the boundaries of reason. Although I find it difficult to appreciate I do understand that when Prince Dara left Lahore with an army of seventy thousand horse, five thousand mounted matchlock men, three thousand mounted archers, ten thousand infantry, over two hundred war elephants, six thousand diggers, five thousand stone-cutters and sappers, he also took along a hundred mullahs to beseech God daily for his victory. Priests praying for their prince's success at arms are a part of every army, though a hundred of them might seem excessive. With somewhat greater difficulty, owing no doubt to my Christian faith, I can also countenance that like many other commanders, the prince did not rely on God's help alone but also pressed Satan into his service by employing several sorcerers to generate worms in the food of the besieged Persian garrison in the Kandahar fort. But any rational man can only shake his head in disbelief when he hears about other instances of the Wali Ahad's superstitious nature and his deep faith in the occult, as also his offensive behaviour towards his senior commanders, which are detailed in the *Lataif-ul-akhbar*, a trustworthy source on the Kandahar campaign even if, understandably, its author chose to remain anonymous.

In the three months that the prince's army held siege of the fort at Kandahar, there appeared, among others, a renowned Tantrik who promised to summon forty genies, *deo*s as the Indians call them, and dispatch them to pull down the fort's walls; a *yogi* accompanied by forty long-haired and bearded disciples, clad in no more than strips of cloth that make a pretence of covering their private parts, who offered to perform a special prayer that would secure the submission of the Persian garrison within twenty days; and a group of sadhus from Kashmir undertaking to build for the prince a wonderful contraption, which would fly through air without wings and could carry three soldiers armed with grenades. The prince welcomed and entertained them all, falling prey to their incredible claims and indulging their unending demands.

The account involving a sorcerer who claimed he could silence the guns and muskets of the Persians for three hours with his incantations, time enough for the soldiers to capture the fort, is particularly entertaining. The magician demanded a fee of twenty rupees and said he would require two dancing girls, one buffalo, a lamb, five cocks, two gamblers and two thieves in order to perform the necessary rites. The sorcerer declared that he had been inside the fort in an invisible form and would lead the soldiers there at an auspicious hour. On the night after, he performed his diabolical rites in the presence of the prince and his favourite commander, Mirza Jafar, throwing grains into a fire as he danced around it, now jumping a yard in the air, now rolling on the ground, and then sacrificed a dog as also the lamb and the cocks he had asked for earlier. To the dancing girls, gamblers and thieves he said, 'It is obligatory to sacrifice you all. However, I shall give my own blood and set you free.' He then stabbed his thigh with a knife and sprinkled drops of his own blood on the blood of the slain animals before he began his weird dance again. Finally, he instructed Mirza Jafar to wash his sword in the sacrificial blood, claiming this would empower the sword to cut through steel and transform its owner into a veritable Achilles without the accursed heel.

Early next morning, when Mirza Jafar went to the sorcerer's tent to wake him up so he could silence the Persian guns before the assault was carried out, the fraud told the bewildered commander, 'Mirza, three powerful *deo*s are guarding the fort. I have struggled with them the entire night. I fought them in the air and on the ground. I have now subdued two who are in my captivity, but the third remains undefeated. Let the attack be postponed till next Monday, once he has been captured.' Of course, on the appointed Monday, the sorcerer revealed that he had been unable to round up the third genie who had proved to be much too strong and, in fact, the sorcerer's own life was in grave danger unless he released the other two genies, and recommended that the whole enterprise be abandoned!

Upon hearing of this turn of events, the prince is said to have asked the veteran general, Mahabat Khan, a slow-paced, grizzled bear of a man, 'The breaches have been opened. What do you advise about an assault?'

'We are servants,' Mahabat Khan replied. 'We are only there to carry out your orders. Only kings can advise kings.'

Dara began with flattery, but ended with harsh words.

'Why do you not say plainly that attack is advisable and that you will fight shoulder to shoulder with the others towards victory? Your father captured the famous fort of Daulatabad and you seem to think of returning home without capturing Kandahar. You will do well to banish such a vain and mischievous idea from your mind.'

Next, the prince asked Najabat Khan to give his opinion on the feasibility of an assault. The commander had recently regained prince's favour after a disgraceful defeat at the hands of the queen of Kumaon, a warrior who had a fondness for cutting off the noses of enemies she captured in battle. Najabat Khan submitted that it would be better if the guns were employed for a further three or four days to punch holes through the walls of the fort. Dara looked at Najabat Khan, tapping his own nose in a message that was as clear to everyone at the meeting as it was insulting to the commander. 'You seem to insinuate that no breaches have been affected. Whether or not there is a breach, an assault must be delivered.'

Then he had turned to Raja Jai Singh of Jaipur and said, 'Raja-ji, your exertions in the emperor's business have fallen short of expectations from the very start. No plea will be heard now. If your objection is that no breach has been made in front of your battery, I give you Jafar's.'

Declining the offer, the raja said, 'By the time Jafar enters through the breach, I shall be able to do the same by fixing scaling-ladders to the wall.'

'If so, when do you propose to deliver the attack?'

'I have nothing to do with agreements and assurances. I have to simply obey your command,' Jai Singh replied.

'What words are these?' the prince had cried out in passion. 'You must say plainly whether an assault is advisable or not. If you mean to keep yourself aloof from the affair, give it to me in writing so that

I may either order a retreat to Hindustan or recall Rustam Khan and initiate an attack with his advice.'

'I am prepared to give in writing that I am always in favour of an attack, and always ready to deliver it,' the raja said.

'Your heart and tongue do not seem to agree,' Prince Dara had retorted. 'What is in your heart your tongue does not reveal, and what your tongue utters finds no echo in your heart. Perhaps it has not occurred to you that I shall return without conquering Kandahar,' he continued. 'If I do so, how can I show my face to the emperor?'

The raja had bridled. 'Your Highness is the very light of the emperor's eyes. Whenever his glance lights upon your face, it will be welcomed. But how shall we humble servants show *our* faces?' he said.

'You have twice shown this very face to His Majesty,' the prince sarcastically remarked. 'The difficulty is mine, for whom this will be the first occasion to do so.'

Jai Singh's face had flushed. The ends of his moustache, the proud accoutrement of a Rajput, quivered.

'Whether you agree or disagree, I command you to make an assault, no matter if you die while conquering the fort.'

As Jai Singh was leaving, Dara said in a voice loud enough to be overheard that the raja looked like a *mirasi*, a minstrel. This was a deadly insult to Rajput honour, implying that the man was only capable of holding a lute in his hands, not a sword.

It is thus untrue, a falsehood given currency by Dara's partisans, that all idolater rajas loved Dara and considered him as one of their own; I cannot imagine that Raja Jai Singh, a proud Rajput, ever forgot that the prince had called him a *mirasi* or bore him any affection thereafter.

A few days later, watched by Prince Dara from the shelter of a house on top of a hill, the Mogul army finally attacked the fort and was met by withering crossfire from the Persian cannon and musketry. After four hours of fighting, the loss of sixteen hundred men and an equal number being wounded, the Indians retreated. Within the fort, the Persians played their trumpets and kettle drums announcing their victory and, to mock the defeated Moguls, they brought dancing girls to perform within sight of the Mogul batteries. The next day, the Persian commander allowed the imperial army to carry away and bury the dead bodies of the Mohammedans while the heads of five hundred idolater soldiers were cut off and heaped together in the fort, leaving the headless trunks to the vultures.

On his return from the failed campaign, the Wali Ahad was accorded a grand reception by the emperor in the audience hall of the Red Fort in the newly constructed city of Delhi where the prince's favourite commanders were honoured with additional titles and rich presents. It seems that given the Mogul army's earlier failures under Aurangzeb on the same mission and the general lack of success against the Persians in recent times, no one took the retreat from Kandahar seriously. Except, perhaps, Prince Dara himself, whose overweening vanity could not bear the slightest dent in the self-image of perfection he had assiduously cultivated throughout his life.

'The larger part of my misfortune probably lay in a constellation of planets that had long ago linked my fate to that of Prince Dara'

NICCOLAO MANUCCI

THE THREE YEARS THAT I spent at the court of the Wali Ahad were also the best period in the noble prince's life. His one failure till that time, the military expedition to recapture the fort of Kandahar, was by now forgotten. The gathering clouds of the struggle for the empire, visible to any wise Amir, were still too far off to be an immediate cause for concern. Showered with honours, his golden throne placed just below the emperor's, the prince was the ruler of India in all but name.

The source of the Wali Ahad's high spirits was neither the ever-increasing signs of his father's favour nor the authority to reign over a great empire. He certainly enjoyed the exercise of power, but what gave him the greatest joy and made him feel most alive were his flights of inspiration as a scholar of religions. I do not quite understand the pleasures of scholarly work and I have even less use for religion than for scholarship—religion never filled a poor man's belly or warmed a lonely man's bed. I do not see the point of delving into dusty tomes to then produce one yourself since it will merely be fated to gather dust. But friends who are scholars tell me that the pleasure of such an exercise is akin to what a doctor feels when he arrives at the correct diagnosis and treatment of a disease that his colleagues have declared incurable. It is, they tell me, very much like the elation one feels when a misty vision suddenly clears up or one gains sight of something that was earlier only sensed. It is the ecstasy one experiences when tediously gathered details retreat into the background and their larger connection stands out for the very first time. But if one wanted to prosper at the prince's court, it was best to show an interest in both.

Much to my relief, I did not need to pretend for too long. In spite of my lack of education, I discovered myself warming to the heat of religious discussions. There was much I did not understand, yet my incomprehension was not an obstacle. Rather, it was a spur, a promise that one day I too will be a part of the conversations that give rise to so much pleasure and excitement.

How do I describe the brilliance of the evenings I spent at the Wali Ahad's mansion, where poetry flowed as liberally as wine; where the naked Sufi poet Sarmad sat on the same carpet as the richly robed and bejewelled Wazir Khan; where, on his rare visits to the capital, Mullah Shah, the prince's spiritual mentor, was received with the honour otherwise reserved for the emperor; where we applauded with genuine delight as the Wali Ahad sang a lullaby he had composed for his war elephant, Fateh Jang; where our frequent laughter dissolved all differences in status but never our mutual respect?

During my time at his court, the prince was at work on his greatest literary essay. With the help of select Hindu scholars he was translating into Persian the fifty-nine *Upanishads*, the scriptures that contain the core of Hindu philosophy. He was convinced that the *Upanishads* were the 'hidden books' alluded to in the Quran. His chief helper in this enterprise was one whom I had seen when I was first presented to the prince in his palace, the famed Maratha scholar Kavindracharya Saraswati.

For all his scholarship, Kavindracharya was a young man, no more than a decade older than I. His head was shaven. He was always clad in a single length of white or saffron-coloured cloth wrapped around his waist, with one end thrown over a shoulder. Normally reserved, if not cold and remote, he thawed when I told him of my studies with the Hindu doctor in Goa.

'Ah, yes, our best doctors live in Goa,' he said.

I asked him some questions about Hindu religion. He answered them politely enough, but I understood from his responses and the way his thin lips seemed to lose any softness that he found my questions naïve. His innate courtesy prevented him from being openly dismissive. He became animated only once, when I spoke of my difficulty with Hindu idolatry.

'Idols are not gods, Niccolao,' he explained, 'but aspects of the Divine. They are the symbols of the many different paths the human soul takes in its attempts to approach the infinite. They are the bridges men need to enter the unknowable realm of the Divine. Would a father, whom his child has never seen, be angry if he returned one day and saw himself being adored as an idol in which the child sees his imaginary form?'

After this exchange Kavindracharya warmed towards me. When we passed each other on the palace grounds he often stopped to ask me about my patients and discuss the methods of treatment I used. Inevitably, both of us gravitated towards the riverbank when we were on our own—I from an atavistic Venetian affinity to water and Kavindracharya because he missed the Ganges which flowed by his home in Benares. I think Kavindracharya opened up to me because he was flattered that I showed genuine interest in the questions I asked him about Hindus and their religious beliefs. He was a recognized authority on both.

It was Kavindracharya who told me that Hindus looked upon the Wali Ahad as the reincarnation of his great-grandfather, Emperor Akbar. He patiently explained that Prince Dara was similar to Akbar

in advocating peace among different religions but went further than
Akbar in his attempts to demonstrate their essential unity.

'Emperor Akbar was a rationalist, dismissive of what he perceived
as absurdities of Islam, of the Hadiths, the Traditions of the Prophet.
He often remarked that only simpletons mistake the traditions of the
ancients for the dictates of reason and are thus condemned to eternal
perdition. The Wali Ahad's writings, on the other hand, are full of
quotations from the Quran and the Hadiths. The Wali Ahad does not
reject religious faith. He is not a rationalist but is a mystic who believes
the Quran and the Hindu Vedas to be revealed texts.'

Emperor Akbar had dismissed the story of the Prophet's physical
ascension, an article of faith for the orthodox, as absurd because of its
physical impossibility. Other Islamic rationalists had tried to arrive
at a compromise by asserting that it was the Prophet's subtle body
that was involved in the ascension, and not his physical body. Prince
Dara took the orthodox position but gave it a Hindu flavour. He said
that in the cave of Hira on the mountain called Jabal Al-Nur in Arabia,
where the Prophet Mohammed received his first revelations through
the angel Gabriel, he had practised controlled breathing, *pranayam* as
Hindu *yogis* call it. This Yogic exercise resulted in his body becoming
lighter than air and more transparent than a diamond. Why, then, was
the Prophet's ascension to the seventh heaven in his rarified physical
body considered an impossibility?

These beliefs and the support he lent to the Hindu subjects of the
kingdom had led to widespread doubts regarding the Wali Ahad's
commitment to Islam. But when I mentioned this to Kavindracharya
he was quick to dismiss the idea of the prince being an apostate. 'No,
our prince is a good Muslim, although not an orthodox Sunni who
piously cleaves to the letter of faith. He is a Sufi who goes beyond the
letter of the Quran to its spirit, and in so doing he has discovered that
the spirit of Islam is identical to that of our *Upanishads*. This scandalizes
the mullahs and orthodox Muslims, especially since the prince does
not keep the Sufi mysteries secret but impetuously broadcasts them
to all and sundry.'

It was common knowledge in the Wali Ahad's court that Mullah Shah would sometimes get irritated with the prince because he was not more circumspect, and constantly advised him to be discreet. 'Inwardly, every act of ours should conform to our own reality and outwardly all acts should be like those of people at large,' he said. But Prince Dara prided himself on being a plain speaker, in banishing ambiguity from his communications. In open fora, like the imperial court, he would declare that the Sharia laws were in conformity with the use and facility of mankind in general and not of Muslims alone. He flouted the strict rules relating to prayer and fasting and countered the criticism from the pious of his wine drinking by repeating Mullah Shah's unorthodox interpretation of the Quranic verse: 'O, you who believe, don't approach prayer when you are drunk.'

'What it means,' Prince Dara said, 'is that if the drunkenness is earthly, the prayer is forbidden out of respect for the prayer. If the intoxication is that of God, then the prayer is forbidden out of respect for the intoxication.'

Following the direction of Kavindracharya's thoughts, I too began to closely observe the prince's activities. I soon realized that if Hindus loved the Wali Ahad it was not just because of the prince's spiritual explorations, or his genuine respect for and admiration of their religion, but for his active interventions on their behalf. It was apparent, even to a recent arrival like me, that Emperor Shah Jahan was a bigot and had been one all his life. The stories of his intolerance were recounted in hushed tones all over the kingdom. In the early years of his reign, every act of intolerance and bigotry had had his approval: conversion of ancient temples into mosques, destruction of Hindu idols and the inexplicable ban on the ringing of temple bells, not to speak of the harsh punishments meted out to those who refused to convert to Islam. The emperor was even said to have applauded his younger son Aurangzeb for 'cleansing Bundelkhand of infidels and infidelity' and making it a hell for non-Muslims after that prince had captured the Rajput kingdom.

In the last twenty years, however, under the growing influence of Prince Dara and Princess Jahanara, the emperor had not himself ordered the destruction of any Hindu temple. And when the zealot Aurangzeb, during his governorship of Gujarat, desecrated the ancient temple of Chintaman by sacrificing cows within the temple grounds and then converting it into a mosque, the noble Prince Dara used his influence with the emperor to restore the temple to the Hindus. Such restoration of idol worship in a place where the cry of the muezzin had recently been heard and the faithful knelt in prayers was without precedent in the history of Mogul rule. There was little doubt that the incident left Aurangzeb—who had taken upon himself the responsibility of restoring the purity of his faith and establishing a rigidly Islamic state—cold with fury. In fact, it further added to the storehouse of Aurangzeb's rage against his elder brother. In indignant letters to the emperor, the young prince warned the emperor that Prince Dara was gnawing at the roots of Islam in Hindustan; he was patronizing Hindu pandits and had surrounded himself with Hindu friends. 'Suffer an infidel to be equal to you and from that moment he will be your superior,' he had written to his father. 'Remove your boot from the top of the head of a snake and it will rear up to bite.' Emperor Shah Jahan ignored Aurangzeb's missives.

On many occasions, the Wali Ahad went out of his way to intercede on behalf of the Hindu subjects of the empire. He was said to have pleaded for leniency for a Hindu *mansabdar* who was accused of keeping a Muslim concubine, a crime that carried the death sentence. But the prince's greatest public act in aid of Hindus was to use his influence in securing the remission of the hated pilgrim-tax in the Hindu holy sites of Allahabad and Benares. For the latter, the prince was instrumental in persuading Kavindracharya to lead a deputation to plead the Hindu case in the imperial court. He coached Kavindracharya so well and the scholar spoke so eloquently that it is said there were tears in the emperor's eyes when he finished. Father Malpica, who came into contact with the Hindus much more than I, told me that with this act Prince Dara had gained a place in Hindu hearts which even Emperor Akbar had not occupied.

And the Muslims? I am only acquainted with the views of ordinary Muslims I met in the taverns which I continued to frequent in spite of my recent elevation. If some of them were uneasy about the Wali Ahad it was not entirely because they believed the dire warnings of their mullahs of the danger he posed to Islam. They felt the prince's attitude and actions threatened their status. Under Mogul rule, except for a short period during Emperor Akbar's reign, it was possible for even the most wretched Muslim to feel superior to a socially elevated Hindu simply because the former was a follower of the Prophet. And when it came to a certain social obligation, he belonged to the master race even if his circumstances were ever so miserable. For in India, as much as in Europe, there is one part of life where the ruler–subject relationship can never be hidden: marriage, the surest indicator of which community is dominant and which subordinate in any society. A Muslim who belonged to the lowest strata of society would never consider giving his daughter in marriage to a Hindu, however high the latter's status may have been. When Emperor Jehangir, generally tolerant and more liberal than his son Shah Jahan, learnt that a Muslim community in Kashmir was giving their daughters to Hindus, he was so incensed that he forbade the practice on penalty of death. Hindu princes gave their women to Moguls as wives or concubines. Some of the proudest Rajput kings, such as those of Jaipur, even considered it an honour to send their daughters or sisters to be part of the emperor's harem. The reverse was unthinkable.

There were exceptions, of course, stories that have become the stuff of legend. In Emperor Jehangir's time, the French physician Bernard fell deeply in love with a dancing girl. After he had effected a remarkable cure of an inmate of the royal harem, the emperor asked him what he would like as his reward. Bernard boldly claimed the girl. The assembled Omrah smiled at a request that was unlikely to be granted since the girl was Muslim. Jehangir, however, surprised everyone by ordering that the girl be seated on the doctor's shoulders and that he carry her away.

During my time at the court, there was another such exception. Jagannath Pandit was a renowned Brahmin scholar from Telangana. He was the author of highly regarded treatises and was patronized by many rajas. I had, in fact, seen him seated next to Kavindracharya on the evening I was first presented at Prince Dara's court. Jagannath became infatuated with a beautiful slave girl in the emperor's harem. In a verse dedicated to her, he addressed her as his 'doe-eyed Lavangi with well-shaped breasts and body as delicate as butter'. Shunning offers of elephants, horses, land and riches, he persisted in asking for Lavangi. Finally, the Wali Ahad intervened on his behalf and Jagannath's heart's desire was fulfilled. But this story did not end happily. Jagannath was maligned and taunted by other Brahmin scholars for marrying a Muslim. In the beginning he defended himself by writing the work *Aniyoktivilas*, which satirized his foes. But the ostracism by his peers gradually wore down his spirit and blighted the couple's love. He and Lavangi committed suicide by drowning themselves in the Ganges at Benares.

I am a fair man. I have witnessed the Moguls treating Hindus very poorly and also with great consideration. The way they behave with Hindus varies from one province to another. Kashmir has very little bigotry; the Punjab a great deal. It also varies with the character of the governor. There are Mogul nobles known for their extreme courtesy, even in dealing with Hindus. There are others like Husain Khan, the governor of Lahore who once remarked that he almost died from shame because he had greeted a Hindu civilly—from the way the man was dressed, Husain Khan had thought him to be a Muslim. To avoid such social disasters in the future, the governor ordered that Hindus were to sew a patch of cloth, different in colour from the rest of their garments, on the underside of the sleeves. He further ordained that in accordance with the Holy Law, the infidels could no longer ride on saddles but would have to sit on pack saddles while journeying on horseback.

Here it would be remiss for me not to admit that men are essentially the same everywhere. At any time in history and in any place, the powerful have always treated the powerless like lower forms of life. My own land boasts of itself as *Libertas Veneziana*, 'Venice, state of liberty'—which is a complete myth. The majority of Venetians, the poor, have no rights, and the nobles and 'citizens' treat them like dirt. In this respect, the only difference between my land and Mogul India is that we belong to the same faith, and religious persecution is not included in our burden of oppression.

In the three years I spent in Prince Dara's court, my name had become well-known in the court circles. My practice was flourishing. I had adopted the strategy of refusing to see too many patients, further increasing the number who wished to be treated by me. Though complicated cases still perplexed me at times, my run of success continued through a combination of luck and good advice from a young Hindu doctor, whom I had employed as an assistant to prepare medicines according to the Hindu system.

I believe it was during the incredibly hot summer of 1657 that my luck began to desert me. There were many minor factors that contributed to my ill-luck, but as the Hindus would say, the larger part of my misfortune probably lay in a constellation of planets that had long ago, perhaps even in a previous birth, linked my fate to that of Prince Dara.

Eager to complete his translation of the *Upanishads*, the Wali Ahad did not accompany the emperor when the latter retreated to the Himalayan foothills to escape the unbearable heat of the plains. The mounting temperatures and his absorption in his work led the prince to dispense with our daily attendance at his court. I presented myself before him only when I was called upon, and that was seldom.

During the exceptionally hot summer, there was a surge in cases of spirit possession. This is perfectly logical if, like the Indians, one believes that spirits are demons from hell and thus presumably at ease with its fires. My preparations for exorcism in the harems of two important Omrah involved finding out more about my patients from members of their households. My experience had proved that this was the best guide to the method I would use to summon and talk to the spirits. If I knew a woman's story, I could intuitively use the right mix of threats and blandishments in forcing the spirit to leave her body. In my preoccupation with the tasks at hand, I paid scant attention when Maria said that she expected to soon have a client for the special ointment. By the time I found out who the client was and could put a stop to the hazardous transaction, it was too late. The delivery had already been promised and two large strings of the finest Basra pearls received as a token of what we could expect if the result was success.

Prince Dara was so faithful to his first wife, Nadira Begum, that few people were aware he was also married to Meher Begum. Renowned for her beauty, Meher Begum was originally a dancing girl. The story goes that in his youth the prince fell deeply in love with her. Rana-dil—that was her original name—was firm that if the prince wanted her to voluntarily offer herself to him he would have to marry her. The emperor refused to give his consent to such an outrageous match. His passion unslaked, the prince sulked and pined till the emperor finally gave in and agreed to the marriage. This was twenty years ago when Meher Begum was nineteen. The Wali Ahad's passion lasted a full six months before he returned to Nadira Begum. All his eight children were born of her. He was unfailingly polite to Meher Begum whenever he came across her in the harem but rarely shared her bed again. In this matter, as in others, Prince Dara did not show any respect for the Sharia, which enjoins upon the Believer to treat all his wives equally.

It had been some months since the prince had visited Meher Begum's apartment and she had decided that she needed to be prepared if the impending visit should spill over into the night. The chances of such an occurrence were slim but always a possibility. Maria's mysterious ointment was her last hope of reviving some of her husband's youthful passion for her.

I do not know if I made an error in instructing my assistant on the right proportion of the ingredients for the ointment—jasmine flowers, marjoram, hemp, buffalo milk and a secret ingredient whose name I do not wish to disclose—or if he made a mistake in its preparation, as I later insisted. The unfortunate result was that a rash of reddish pustules erupted on the outer and inner lips of Meher Begum's vulva, where she had applied the ointment. Within a day, these filled up with pus and began to give off a most disagreeable odour that could not be disguised by even the strongest attar. The harem was in uproar. Prince Dara ordered the head eunuch to probe into the circumstances of the affair. The Aitmad did not seek the medical testimony of the court hakims, but turned instead to a French physician recently arrived in Delhi, a M. Bernier.

Both Maria and I were banned from the harem till investigations were completed and the Begum was on her way to full recovery. I was to learn only later that this M. Bernier had had the gall to call me a quack, a quack who had brought shame to Europeans in India and dishonour to European medicine! He had, in fact, gone so far as to recommend that I be struck by a hundred lashes of the kora on my back and be thrown out of the Mogul dominions. This from a man whose own education, I was to later discover, was a three-month condensed course in medicine, which qualified him as a doctor on the condition that he would never seek to practise on French national territory!

M. Bernier's intemperate attack dented my reputation somewhat, but could not do it lasting damage. Some of my former patients belonged to the highest circles of Mogul nobility and were prepared to bear personal witness to my healing skills. Prince Dara too did not doubt my explanation that my assistant had made a mistake in the preparation of the ointment. I compensated my assistant generously while regretfully dismissing him from my service. I also convinced the prince that I had been unaware of the intended user of the ointment. This was a deception Maria had urged on me.

'My little Nicco,' she had said tenderly. 'I cannot escape punishment for procuring the ointment for Meher Begum. But why should you suffer too?'

The Wali Ahad was a most compassionate prince. Maria was neither imprisoned nor physically chastised, but only banished from the empire. The punishment was as much for her liaison with me while being a member of the harem as for supplying the ill-fated ointment. I was devastated at the thought of our separation. What I had taken to be a convenient arrangement to satisfy my base desires had, unbeknownst to me, wormed its way into my heart. How often did I need to be taught that the soul's longing cannot be cut off from the body's desire!

Maria left for Goa, and when I next received news of her a little over eight months later it was of her marriage to a Portuguese officer. Strange, that after all we had shared as companions in body and deed, the thought of living with each other as husband and wife had not crossed our minds. I often think that we hesitated on that count because our situations as *farangis* at the Mogul court made us cautious and taught us not to declare our feelings too early and regret them too late. But, perhaps, what really prevented us from becoming a couple was what had brought us so close: our mutual intoxication with physical love. It fertilized our tenderness, yes, but also hastened its growth so that the roots remained weak and could be easily torn up.

'The rot starts, as it always does, from the top: as they say in France, "A fish always starts smelling from the head"'

FRANCOIS BERNIER

IN MY OBSERVATIONS OF the Indies I believe I have redeemed an unspoken pledge to M. Gassendi by informing my patrons and esteemed readers in France on the manners and mores of the people. I am equally satisfied that my observations are not hearsay but based on personal observation during my years of service with Danishmand Khan, reinforced by testimony obtained from reliable natives and Europeans familiar with the Indies, especially the four Jesuit missionaries who, when I arrived, had already lived in the country for more than fifteen years and whom I visited often before their unfortunate exile to Agra.

Indians may be polite and friendly and possess other admirable personal qualities, but their public life is marred by sycophancy and corruption, which a European will find base and revolting. The rot starts, as it always does, from the top: as they say in France, 'A fish always starts smelling from the head.' I have witnessed several instances of such disgusting adulation at the morning court of the monarch. There is, it seems, no Mogul who has not grown up with this Persian proverb repeatedly dinned into his ears:

'If the monarch says the day is night

Reply: The moon and stars are shining bright.'

When the emperor says something, however trifling be his words, the Omrah extend their arms heavenwards as if anticipating benediction and cry out in a chorus, '*Karamat! Karamat!* (Wonderful! Wonderful!)' Father Roth, a German Jesuit priest who became my friend and was also close to Niamat Ali, a senior eunuch in the monarch's household, had reported that the same words are repeated by the emperor's personal attendants when he happens to loudly break wind during his morning ablutions—and I have no reason to doubt Father Roth's report.

The voice of flattery pervades all ranks of society. When a Mogul has occasion for my services, he begins with the preamble that I am the Aristotle, Hippocrates and the Avicenna of the age. In the beginning, I protested against such a fulsome mode of address by attempting to assure people that I was very far from possessing the merits they attributed to me and found such comparisons highly embarrassing. But finding that my modesty only increased the intensity of their praises, I became determined to close my ears to their flattery as I had done to their discordant music.

The idolaters, servile by nature from centuries of oppression by their own princes as much as by the Mohammedans, are even worse than the Moguls in the extent to which they stretch their sycophancy. I shall relate only one anecdote to illustrate what I mean. One of their learned pandits, as scholars of Gentile laws are called, whom I had introduced into the Agha's service, once began his panegyric to Danishmand Khan by comparing him to the greatest conquerors the world has known. His nauseous observations ended with these words, uttered in all seriousness: 'When you, my Lord, place your foot in the stirrup, to mount your horse and march at the head of your cavalry, the earth trembles. The eight elephants on whose heads the earth rests find it impossible to support the extraordinary weight.'

At the conclusion of this speech I put on a suitably grave face and told the Agha that it behooved him to be careful about how he mounted his horse since Delhi could not afford any more earthquakes which caused so much devastation.

'Yes, my friend,' he said with a smile, 'and that is the reason why I generally choose to be carried in a litter.'

The Agha possessed a subtle, dry sense of humour although he rarely displayed it and, then, only to those whom he had admitted to familiarity.

Yet, Danishmand Khan was a Mogul too, although of Persian birth, and however astute his intellect and discerning his judgement he was not totally immune to flattery's insidious charm. While rejecting it with his head, he could not help his heart's thirst for admiration, regardless of the ugliness of the vessel and the baseness of its carrier. Perhaps Indians are more susceptible to this all-too-human weakness and rightly believe that there can never be too much sycophancy; if you scatter enough around, some of it will always find its target.

If flattery is the coin of social discourse, then corruption is the currency of all transactions in the regime. This is easily evident in the number of words they have for a bribe in their language—*dastoor, nazrana, baksheesh*, and so on. It is an established custom throughout the country that without the intercession of influential friends or the payment of bribes nothing gets done; even princes of royal blood cannot get their work done without making some kind of payment. Bribes are, in fact, such an accepted part of life that if a courtier asks the king for a favour on behalf of a general or officer, be it an appointment or transfer, the king never neglects to ask how much money the former has received. The courtier ordinarily admits the exact amount and after leaving a portion of the bribe with the intercessor, the king takes the rest for himself and sends it off to the treasury.

Surprisingly, it is not the lack of good laws that is responsible for the state of affairs. If properly administered, the existing laws would render the Indies as eligible a residence as any nation in Europe. But of what use are good laws if they are not observed and when there is no possibility of enforcing them? The sole aim of governors of provinces appointed by the king is to amass as much wealth as they can in the time they have left in their appointments before they are removed by the whim of the monarch or the machinations of enemies at the court. The magistrates, or *kadi*s, and other officers of the state, follow the example set by the governor. If justice is ever administered, it is among the lower classes, among persons who, being equally poor, have no means of corrupting the judge or buying false witnesses who can be acquired in great numbers and at a cheap rate. The only hope of impartial justice is from the emperor himself, who has a reputation as a just ruler. But how is a poor peasant to defray the expense of a journey to Delhi in the hope of presenting his case at the court? My account, I know, is possibly at variance with those of some other travellers who have extolled the quickness of the judicial system of the Moguls. They have perhaps only witnessed the summary proceedings in a court where two poor men were hurried out to be dispensed hard blows on the soles of their feet. Unless the parties were lucky and were immediately dismissed by the *kadi* with the soft words, '*Musalih Baba* (Be at peace my children)', though without being given a hearing. Moreover, if the party in the wrong possessed the means to put a couple of crowns in the hands of the police, the *kadi* and his clerks, or had enough money to buy two false witnesses, he would win his case or be in a position to prolong it for as long as he pleased.

Given my irritation at the servile attitude of my interlocutors and their utter disregard for rational discourse (which was almost always a feature of my encounters with the idolaters) providing an objective account of the race that constitutes the vast majority of India's population requires considerable effort on my part. They are so numerous, in fact, that there are five or six idolaters for every Mohammedan. It is astonishing to see how this enormous multitude has allowed itself to be subjected by so small a number of Mohammedan princes. But the amazement disappears when one remembers that the idolaters are not a united race and that their religion, which in reality is no more than gross superstition, has introduced such a diversity of opinions and customs among them that they seldom agree with each other.

This is not to say that the Moguls themselves have a great sense of unity. As a doctor who was also once attached to a Mogul army, I have seen its units of foreign mercenaries, often representing a dozen Mohammedan lands, function like tribes keen to maintain their autonomy in an unwieldy mass of irregulars. I have been witness to the mutual jealousy of the petty nobles called *mansabdars* that makes it impossible for them to execute coordinated plans in attack or defence unless the prince at the head of the army commands both respect and fear. Five and twenty thousand of our veterans from the army in Flanders, commanded by Prince Conde, would easily overcome these oriental armies, however enormous. But, when confronted by infidels, the Moguls can bank on the solidarity and common patriotism engendered by their faith. Idolaters, though, are as impervious to appeals to religious unity as they are to the fate of their rulers, since, beaten down through centuries by tyrants, homegrown or foreign, all they desire is to be left in peace and, if that is not possible, then to merely survive.

The divisions within the idolaters are so marked that of them will eat bread or drink water in a house belonging to a person of a different caste, unless it is nobler and more exalted than his own. These castes are like the tribes once were among the Jews, and although it is commonly believed that there are seventy-two of these castes I have ascertained from pandits that idolaters can be reduced to four principal castes from which all others derive their origin. The second caste, below the Brahmins, that of the warrior Rajputs, is the only division that is brave and distinguished in the profession of arms. If united, they could have disputed the rule of the Moguls but their rajas, who are like so many petty kings, are constantly scheming or fighting against one another and it is their disunion that has made them tributaries to the Great Mogul. The Kachhwahs of Jaipur and the Rathors of Jodhpur do not display half as much zest in fighting the Safavids of Persia or the Moguls of Delhi as they do in opposing the Sisodias of Udaipur.

Most of the Rajput princes are now in the emperor's service and are firm supporters of the empire. The Mogul emperor recompenses some of the principal rajas by paying them handsome salaries and giving them generous presents, and binds them even closer to the throne by taking their princesses into the seraglio as wives.

The Mohammedans rightly despise the idolaters as a naïve and primitive people who have no conception of God as the Creator of the world but believe in hundreds of god and goddesses. They worship these beings, both divine and demonic, many of them no more than gargoyles, some with multiple arms, others with bulging eyes and lolling tongues, or even with faces of animals—a lion, an elephant, a boar or a monkey—in garishly painted stone idols. They placate spirits in trees by making offerings of flowers and grains of rice.

Partly on my solicitation and partly to gratify his own curiosity, the Agha, had taken into his service one of the most celebrated pandits in the Indies who had once belonged to the household of Prince Dara and who introduced me to the other pandits he attracted to the house. I tried to understand their beliefs but found that I got a headache whenever the pandits tried to explain something to me.

Every idolater belief, every idolater law, seems to have its opposite, and the pandits gravely maintained that all of them were equally true. Since they have not had the benefit of our Enlightenment, even their best minds continue to live in an enchanted world, which makes for confused thinking, lacking the clarity of thought of our best thinkers. Never having heard of Descartes, they are lamentably ignorant of basic facts like the impossibility of the coexistence of opposites. Instead of an unambiguous 'yes' or 'no' to a question that can have but one answer, they inevitably slide into rambling discourses which simultaneously communicate assent and dissent. If one were to persist and try to pin them down, their response would be amusing enough: 'We do not pretend that our laws are of universal application. God intended them only for us. We do not even say that yours is a false religion; it may be adapted to your wants and circumstances, for the gods have no doubt appointed many different ways of reaching heaven.' Try as I might, I found it impossible to convince them that the Christian faith was designed for the whole of mankind, and theirs was mere fable and gross fabrication. For instance, they believe that their souls are constituent parts of God and therefore it is, in fact, we humans who have imposed upon ourselves religious worship, belief in paradise and in hell—which is patently absurd. It is impossible to rid idolaters of their errors, because they will not listen to reason and entirely subordinate their judgement to their ancient customs. They are tender-hearted towards animals of every description, save man; they have scruples about killing a snake or even a bug, yet regard it as a highly meritorious action to cause a living woman to be burnt on a pyre, along with the body of her deceased husband. The Mohammedans, at least, are unambiguous and consistent in what they believe, even if that belief be in error, and there is no difficulty in carrying out a conversation or disputation on religious matters with an educated adherent of the Mohammedan faith.

In spite of their subjugated condition and the absurdity of their beliefs, learned idolaters, all of whom belong to the caste of Brahmins, are an arrogant race that holds that when a man is above others in the nobility of his descent, as they are themselves, he also surpasses the rest of mankind in understanding. They assert, relying on this unsound prejudice shared by all idolaters, that only those who are as high-born as Brahmins can know true religion and true science. They state openly that a man of low birth is as despicable as a *farangi*; such a man may be rich and brave but he can never be wise. Just as all that the pandits say about their religion is chimerical and fantastical, so it is with their notions of nobility. I have seen many Brahmins carrying loads on their backs day and night, or working with an axe and doing other acts which are considered humble by Europeans. To this, I must add that a majority of them are illiterate and ignorant and consequently very superstitious, and even the ones who consider themselves to be intellectually superior are no more than arrant sorcerers.

The idolaters are also firm in their belief that they are the only people who are polite in manners and the cleanest and most orderly among all the races. They think that all Europeans are barbarous, disorderly, despicable and filthy. An idolater will sooner die of hunger or thirst than eat a meal prepared by a *farangi* or accept a cup of water from his hands. I must add that whereas I found the accusation of dirtiness against Europeans more amusing than annoying, a similar barb by the Agha distressed me deeply, although I was at pains to hide my anguish from my benefactor. One day, as I entered his presence, I was surprised to see Danishmand Khan, normally a sober man with a grave demeanour, smiling broadly at what was being read out to him from a book by Dost Khan, who often came around in the morning with the latest court gossip. I must add that the pleasure he took in listening to gossip, though without contributing to it, was the Agha's only vice and explained their unlikely friendship.

'Come, Bernier,' Danishmand Khan called to me after I had made my salaams. 'Listen to what our friend has found in an old book. It is the report of the ambassador of Andalus of his visit to the court of a European king. The ambassador is describing his impressions of Europe to his sovereign.'

Dost Khan smiled in complicity, exposing his irregular teeth stained dark brown from the constant chewing of tobacco. Then he began to read aloud from the book, 'The Vikings are the filthiest race God ever created. They do not wipe themselves after going to stool, nor wash themselves any more than if they were wild asses.'

'The Vikings live in the far north of Europe . . . France is in the south,' I hastily said, as both of them peered at me with a mischievous glint in their eyes. 'And this account must be over two hundred years old,' I added weakly.

'Ah, Bernier,' the Agha began to laugh, 'I know Vikings don't live in France.' His easy assumption of superiority angered me, but I reminded myself that the Agha was a most considerate man, infinitely courteous, and that perhaps encouraged by that odious Dost Khan he had permitted himself a rudeness that was quite foreign to his nature.

The Agha's curiosity about European philosophy is not to be confused with his admiration for the European races. The Omrah take it for granted that Islam is the most perfect of religions, or that Mogul cuisine is superior to all others, or that art and poetry of Persian origin are unrivalled by any other nation in the world. At such times, I overlooked the ignorance and condescension in his holding such beliefs and consoled myself that if Danishmand Khan was allowing himself fun at my expense, then it was a sign of his growing familiarity and favour. Indeed, gradually, careful not to excite jealousy among his other employees although I doubt he was entirely successful in that effort, Danishmand Khan did begin to trust me with his affairs and to include me in his entourage during official receptions. On my part, I was happy to serve that most excellent man both as a physician and in carrying out assignments related to his office.

Unlike most Indians, who always search for ways to convert their influence with powerful people at the court into silver and gold, I can truthfully assert that I did not ask for a single rupee when approached for help by a deserving person in need of my services. Thus I readily agreed to put in a word for the Ethiopian ambassador when he turned up at my house one day, half famished and without decent clothing, destitute of money or bills of exchange, having been robbed of all valuables and most of his slaves on his way from Surat to Delhi. He was carrying a letter from M. Briffault, the chief of the French factory and my host at Surat, and narrated his tale of woe. No one else would have exerted himself on behalf of these foreigners who came to Delhi without presents, looking like beggars rather than representatives of an African power. Till I lent them some money to hire a cart, the ambassador and his fourteen-year-old son could be seen traversing the streets on foot, clad in dirty Bedouin robes, followed by their two bare-footed and bare-headed slaves, who had no raiment but a strip of cloth passing through the crack between their buttocks.

I was successful in pleading the Ethiopians' case with Danishmand Khan, who invited the ambassador and his son to his home. Ever in search of new knowledge, the Agha evinced keen interest in the country and the nature of its government. The ambassador was a mine of information on the country and the customs of its people: the worth of a man in Ethiopia, for instance, is estimated by the number of his children; the emperor had fathered over eighty and he was the father of sixteen, including the lad accompanying him, who was his favourite. I concede that after a while I stopped paying attention to the ambassador's talk since I found myself being distracted more and more by his son who sat quietly in a corner. From time to time the boy would exchange quick looks with me in which curiosity, interest and speculation were evident. The lad was remarkably well made; his skin was of the clearest black, his nose was not flat nor his lips thick, and he had the longest eyelashes I have seen on a boy. Danishmand Khan, who noticed my interest—little escaped his keen gaze—and was aware of my predilection in these matters, took me aside one day after the Ethopians had left and told me that he had talked to the ambassador, who had agreed to sell the boy to me for fifty rupees. 'We shall yet make an Amir out of you, Bernier, if not a poet,' he said, patting me on the shoulder and referring to the taste I now shared with men of refinement among upper-class Mohammedans. Here, I should perhaps mention that any European who has spent as much time at the Mogul court as I cannot help but be infused with the easy carnality of the Omrah, which makes little distinction between woman or boy as its object. Suffice to say that the warm springs, hot summers and the fecundity of the earth of the Indies encouraged my soul to bloom with flowers other than the ones found in the gardens of our Holy Church as I reclaimed the heritage of the ancient Greeks.

Danishmand Khan's intervention led to the Ethiopian ambassador being granted an audience at the imperial court. With his usual generosity, the emperor invested the ambassador with a *serapa*, a robe of honour consisting of a brocade vest, an embroidered silk girdle and a turban of the same material. He also gave orders for the maintenance of the Ethiopians as long as they stayed in Delhi and presented the ambassador with six thousand rupees, which is the equivalent of three thousand crowns.

With the change in his circumstances, the ambassador turned out to be an ingrate. He sent word that he would not part with his boy for less than three hundred rupees rather than the contracted fifty. I was furious with him for breaching an agreement he had made with the Agha but paid the three hundred rupees, mostly for the satisfaction of telling people about a father who had sold me his own child. Habshi, as I called the boy after the land of his origin which is also known as Abyssinia, was a lovely, even-tempered lad who provided me much solace during my sojourn in the Indies and after my return to France. He is a handsome young man now, pursued by many Parisian ladies ever on the lookout for new sensations, but remains devoted to me even as he spreads his favours among women; the lad has now become a refined 'man of two tastes' as the Indians would call him.

*'I am more sceptical of Dara's claims about the
fruits of his quest than of its sincerity'*

FRANCOIS BERNIER

IN SUMMER, WITH THE emperor departing for cooler climes, Delhi transforms into a sleepy little provincial town and reveals its real face, otherwise concealed behind the mask of a cosmopolitan city.

I am aware that most inquiries on my return to France will pertain to the capital cities of the Mogul empire and that my patrons and well-wishers will be anxious to know if Delhi and Agra rival Paris in beauty, size and the number of inhabitants. I have prepared, therefore, to gratify the understandable curiosity upon these points by taking careful notes on the surroundings and a few other matters that my readers might find interesting.

Delhi is a city that is made up of parts both very old and very new. The older part consists of ruins of mosques, serais, tombs, tanks, fortifications built by kings of other Mohammedan dynasties that ruled the country before the arrival of the Moguls. These lie scattered over a large area to the south beyond the city walls that is slowly being reclaimed by scrub and jungle and is reputed as being the refuge for bands of robbers who waylay travellers on the highway to the Deccan. The new portion, less than twenty years old, is called Shahjahanabad—after the emperor who built it—but since this name is unknown to Europeans, I shall continue to call the city by its old name.

The emperor had shifted his capital from Agra to Delhi in 1639, citing the scorching summer as the reason for what was still the largest city in the Mogul empire being unfit to be his residence. The real reason, I suspect, was more personal and may have had to do with the death of his favourite wife; after Mumtaz Mahal was no more, the monarch decided to leave Agra and embarked on frenetic construction activity that included the building of the Taj Mahal as well as Shahjahanabad.

Delhi is built in the shape of an imperfect crescent moon on the bank of the river Jamuna. A brick wall has been built to fortify the new capital on all sides except the one defended by the river. It is said that on the advice of an astrologer, Shah Jahan had the heads of hundreds of decapitated criminals deposited in the wall's foundations to ensure that the capital will never be sacked by invaders or its inhabitants put to sword. Tall towers flank the wall at every hundred paces, and it has twelve entrances of which the two main gates open on to the roads to Agra in the east and Lahore in the northwest. I found Delhi's fortifications to be unimpressive since there are neither artillery pieces placed on the towers nor ditches for additional defence. A European battery of moderate force would have little difficulty in breaching the walls.

Between the city and the suburbs the countryside is interspersed with extensive gardens and sprawling fields, and beyond the suburbs are the residences of the great Omrah and the camps of the idolater rajas in service with the Great Mogul. Some of these camps, such as Jaswantpur and Jaisinghpur, named after the Rajput kings of Jodhpur and Jaipur, two generals among the most loyal in the monarch's army, have grown into small townships exclusively inhabited by idolaters.

In France, I had avidly perused accounts of the fabled wealth of the Indies and the magnificence of the Mogul court and was thus sorely disappointed with my first impressions of the capital city of the Mogul empire. Oh, Delhi has some fine avenues and not a few splendid palaces that are in no way inferior to those of the same class in Paris. Its imposing main bazaar, wider and more spacious than any street in any European capital, flanks the road that leads from the emperor's citadel to the Lahore gate and is covered by a high, arched roof with large, round apertures which allow an abundance of air and light to stream in. Outside the walls of the city, are the fine mansions of the Omrah and rich merchants, nestled in luxuriant green foliage, giving them an appearance of castles located in the heart of a forest. In a hot and parched country, where the eye seeks refreshment and repose in verdure, such landscapes are inordinately pleasing. I must also admit that in my experience there is nothing more spectacular in the world than the great Royal Square in front of the emperor's citadel at certain hours of the day when the Omrah, rajas and the *mansabdar*s come to mount guard or to attend court. Dressed in finery and mounted on a fine Turkish horse, even a lowly *mansabdar* is normally escorted by at least four servants, two leading in front and two following behind. The Omrah and the idolater rajas, as befitting their exalted status, come riding on magnificently caparisoned elephants, or are conveyed in richly carved palanquins inlaid with silver or gold leaf, leaning against thick brocade cushions and chewing betel leaves. The palanquins are carried on the shoulders of six men wearing the livery of their masters while a servant walks on one side bearing a spittoon of porcelain or silver and two servants walk on the other side of the palanquin, flapping away flies with peacock-tail fans. Footmen march in front, clearing the way, while a posse of best-mounted horsemen bring up the rear of an Amir's retinue. If I had not regarded this display of magnificence with philosophical indifference, I might have been carried away by such flights of imagination as inspire idolater poets and cause them to represent the royal elephants as conveying not noblemen but goddesses concealed from the vulgar gaze of mortals.

Although Delhi appears very pleasant from afar—the expanses of greenery make it look from a distance more like a thick wood than a

city—one only needs to walk a few hundred metres from the Royal
Square and away from the main bazaar in any direction to see that the
city is an unplanned, chaotic jumble of narrow, overcrowded streets
teeming with men and cattle. Clusters of scabrous slums with their
mean mud houses thatched with straw are home to common troopers
and the vast multitude of servants and camp followers who trail in
the wake of the imperial army. These wretched huts, indiscriminately
scattered throughout the city, easily catch fire and prove to be death
traps, especially during the summer months when dry, hot winds blow
from the desert of Rajputana as from the furnace of hell; I was told
that more than sixty thousand roofs had burnt down in three large
fires the year before I arrived.

If Delhi, which has a population of about half a million, equalling
that of Paris, seems provincial and shabby in comparison to the French
capital, it has to do with three glaringly obvious features. Paris is a
city whereas Delhi is little more than a cantonment, deriving its chief
support from the presence of the court and the army. Almost three
quarters of its population is transient and follows the monarch in his
travels, shrinking the city to a provincial town with less than seventy
thousand inhabitants whenever he undertakes a long campaign to
subdue the many rebellions that constantly flare up in far-flung parts
of his empire.

Then there is the appearance of the people. In Paris, at least seven
out of ten people seen on the street are tolerably well clad and have a
certain air of respectability. Walking down a Parisian street you will
be among swarms of merchants, respectable women out shopping
accompanied by tolerably well-clad servants laden with baskets,
gentlemen in their powdered wigs being carried on sedan chairs by
trotting bearers and, on occasion, even a noble in a great black coach
with gold trimming and high wheels scattering urchins in its path. In
Delhi, for every two passers-by wearing decent apparel, well mounted
and properly attended, there will be eight ragged wretches. In the
capital city of the Indies, a man can either belong to the highest rank
or live miserably; there is no middle ground. Oriental splendour and

the fabled riches are confined to the royal court and those who provide it with luxuries.

Although it is the seat of a mighty empire and home to a splendid court that is a natural magnet for a vast quantity of costly goods from all over the world, Delhi has no streets like St Denis in Paris. The expensive merchandise is generally kept in warehouses and for every shop that displays fine cloth and silks, brocades and turbans embroidered with gold, there are at least twenty-five that stock only the basic necessities required to sustain life: pots of oil, baskets filled with rice, barley, chickpeas, wheat flour and a variety of other grains and pulses.

It is not that the bazaars of Delhi are uniformly dismal. The fruit market, for instance, tries to make some show with dry fruits, such as almonds, pistachios, walnuts, raisins, prunes and apricots imported from Persia, Balkh, Bokhara and Samarkand in summer and fresh black and green grapes of excellent quality brought by Afghan traders in round wooden boxes from the same countries in winter. The main bazaar on the Lahore road and the Royal Square remain perhaps the most captivating spots in the city. Besides the procession of nobles at certain hours of the day, the Royal Square is also the site for a bazaar, held on two days of the week, when shops offering an endless variety of goods are set up for a few hours. Like the Pont-Neuf in Paris, this bazaar is also a rendezvous for beggars, mountebanks, jugglers, as well as fortune-tellers and astrologers to whom the people of the Indies, both Mohammedans and idolaters are extremely partial. Perhaps the difference between the Royal Square of Delhi and Pont-Neuf best captures the difference between the Indies and Europe. The Royal Square derives its glory from ceremonials of the court and short periods of bustling commerce when common people can feel a temporary sense of belonging, if not of ownership. At night, the once-bustling square is deserted, scattered pools of dim light from the guard posts barely outlining the few shadows scurrying across its vast expanse. Contrast this to the view from Pont-Neuf, which is thronged by people and carriages at all hours of the day and night. From the bridge on the

Seine, you can see rows of subdued lights spilling out of innumerable windows of lofty houses until well past midnight. On the streets, lit by long lines of lamps burning with equal constancy in foul and fair weather in every direction, citizens perambulate with their wives and daughters. In the Indies, respectable women, especially those belonging to the nobility, rarely venture out of the seraglios and are never seen unveiled or with their husbands in public.

To be fair, where Delhi scores over Paris is in the relative cleanliness of its main streets, which are swept every day by an army of cleaners. Although their brooms, made from a bunch of thin twigs bound at one end by a length of twine, raise a good deal of dust, it is undeniable that they keep Delhi free of *boue*, the stinking sewage that is spread over the streets of Paris. Unlike Paris, in the capital of the Mogul empire one will not see a well-off citizen walking on the street holding a posy of flowers before his face or a perfumed handkerchief over his nose to keep out the disgusting odour.

I spent the most part of the summer of 1657 reading histories of the Mogul emperors and the books written by Dara Shukoh. The latter was not a diversion I chose but a task the Agha had entrusted to me before he left to join the emperor's retinue.

'You have read many philosophical tracts, Bernier,' he said. 'I want to hear your impressions of the Wali Ahad's writings, not of their content but of the impressions they give of the writer. I would be interested to know the conclusions you arrive at about him from his writings alone.'

The task was challenging and I threw myself into it with energy and resolve, or at least as much energy as I could muster through the unremitting assault of Delhi's summer heat. I was glad to spend the days in my study, its windows covered by mats of moistened, sweet-smelling khus grass that cooled the air to a tolerable level. Habshi wandered in and out of the room quietly, taking care not to disturb my studies, sometimes laying his head in my lap for a little while so I could stroke his woolly hair and the butter-smooth skin of his neck.

My mentor M. Gassendi used to say that the writings of a man, whether poet or scholar, are part of his continuing autobiography; to the right kind of reader a piece of prose or verse is a mirror reflecting the author's life and character. Going by this, I am afraid I may not have been the right kind of reader for Dara Shukoh's literary works. I take pride in my rationality and am a great admirer of Descartes whereas the prince is clearly influenced by the mystical strains of Neo-Platonism. My knowledgeable readers will doubtless be acquainted with the doctrine of a universal Life Principle of which each one of us is a part. This is a doctrine the idolaters in the Indies share with the Sufi sect of Islam and the learned men and poets of Persia. It is similar to beliefs which led the alchemists of Europe hopelessly astray and which have been ably refuted by M. Gassendi.

The basic tenor of the prince's writings conforms to this doctrine: Oneness of God and Man, the immanence of the Divine and the consequent assertion that there is no difference between various religions; they are but different vessels carrying water from the same ocean. He writes in one of his tracts:

> 'Thou art in Kaaba as well as
> in the Somnath temple,
> In the convent and
> in the tavern.
> Thou art at the same time,
> the light and the moth,
> the wine, the cup, the sage and the fool,
> the friend and the stranger.'

Having carefully studied the writings, including such minor works like the *Hasanat-ul-Arifin* in which the prince ventures beyond his Sufi beliefs to openly embrace Gentile influences I can now confidently claim that Dara was no scholar. 'Careful scholarship should not only form the basis of your opinions but must inform even your speculations,' had been M. Gassendi's advice. 'Speculation is the basis of discovery, of progress, but must rest on the secure base of scholarship.' The first three books he wrote are the works of a seeker on the Sufi path: two are on the lives of Sufi saints while the third, *Risala-i-Haqnuma* or 'Compass of Truth', is a set of instructions for novices on the road to wisdom the prince claims to have himself travelled. I cannot judge its content but it is written as though by a devotee, sorely lacking in critical acumen and scientific spirit, seeking not insight but intoxication in ornamental, exalted flights of language which I find distasteful.

Whether one chooses to believe (which I do not) or doubt (which I emphatically do) Dara's assertion that the book was inspired by divine revelation is a matter of personal conviction. In the *Hasnat-ul-Arifin*, the prince popularizes the teachings of the Gentile mystic Baba Lal and reports in detail a long conversation they had had. He approvingly quotes passages from another mystic, Kabir, who believed that the distinctions the Believers draw between *kufr*, unbelief, and Islam, were frivolous. I can quite comprehend the consternation with which pious Muslims received these views and the rage such statements must have aroused in the Mullahs.

In the last book the prince wrote, *Majma-ul-Baharain* or 'Mingling of Two Oceans', in which he seeks to demonstrate that the cosmogony of the idolaters is similar to that of Islam, his scholarship leaves much to be desired; the analogies are farfetched and the parallelisms are superficial. Passages in these books seem to be penned by a religious versifier rather than by a philosopher of religions. Writers of religious verse, I do not hesitate to offer my opinion, are the worst kind of poets, impelled to sing a song that almost never sounds better than a croak.

It was well known among the court circles that the prince was presently busy translating the most important religious book of the idolaters into Persian. In recent years he had been a patron of many such translations and, from my knowledge of Islam, was moving dangerously close to heresy. In his introduction to a book about an idolater god, Rama, composed by a mythical sage, Vashishtha, Prince

Dara writes: 'When I had gone through the Persian translation of this book . . . I saw in a dream two dignified figures of calm appearance, one of them standing on a higher level than the other . . . Vashishtha, with great affection and graciousness, placed his hand on my back and told Ramachandra, "Rama, here is an earnest seeker of knowledge and a brother of yours in true search of Reality; embrace him." Ramachandra held me in his embrace with great warmth and love. Then Vashishtha gave some sweets to Ramachandra which I ate out of his hand. After seeing this dream my desire to have this book translated became greater than ever . . .' I could not imagine the mullahs, guardians of the pure faith, countenance the prince's consorting on such friendly terms with heathen gods, even if it be in a dream.

To be fair, as I reported to the Agha, Dara's writings are sincere, especially in his first book and in passages of *Risala*, where the pain and suffering of a young man who embarks on a spiritual quest in search of the meaning of life, an affliction common although not limited to youth, are touchingly apparent. I am more sceptical of Dara's claims about the fruits of his quest than of its sincerity. The prince's religious practice, which he learnt from his teacher Mullah Shah, consisted of two activities. The first was reciting very slowly the name 'Allah' in his mind, without any movement of the tongue; the second, sitting in meditation, controlling the mind by regulating his breathing, using a method similar to that used by the holy men among idolaters. His gift was so unique, he claimed, that he began to see the light of the soul and hear cosmic sounds within six months of beginning his practice—mystical accomplishments, which, I am informed, normally take an aspirant a lifetime of rigorous observance.

On some evenings, when I wished for intellectually stimulating company as a relief from my solitary labours, I would invite one or more of the Jesuit fathers for dinner. They made interesting companions, especially Father Roth, who shared my interest in philosophy. I had visited the house of the Jesuits once, but after a disagreeable encounter with that Italian quack Manucci, who was their neighbour and had dropped in on the same evening but rudely turned his back and left the house as I entered, without addressing a word to me, I preferred to extend my hospitality to the Jesuits and not presume on theirs.

In the manner of all exiles we conjured up our favourite bits and pieces of Europe while we sipped on indifferent Shiraz wine: crossing the Pont-Neuf in Paris on a summer evening, a long walk in the forest near Baden when the leaves are turning shades of yellow and brown, a dinner at a farmhouse in Tuscany which Father Malpica remembered as the best meal he had had in his life. Warmed by the wine, we were of one mind: that there were more stars in our European sky, more flowers in our European gardens than in this country of abundance.

The evenings were not solely devoted to nostalgia; we spoke also about the state of the country in which we found ourselves visitors. Since the fathers had lived in the Indies for many years and travelled deep into its interiors on missionary work, they were a storehouse of information on the country and the condition of its people.

There are, indeed, some excellent missionaries in this part of the world, especially the Jesuits who meekly impart religious instruction to all without mixing it with an indiscreet and bigoted zeal. But I have had too much intercourse with Indians, both Mohammedan and Gentile, and am too well acquainted with the blindness of the human soul to believe that the conversions the Jesuits seek can be in any large numbers. In the beginning, more than a hundred years ago, the Jesuit fathers who came to Goa in the wake of the Portuguese conquerors and tried to convert the idolaters to the Christian faith were ignorant of the contempt the high-born Gentiles had for Europeans, whom they called *farangi*s. They were unaware that a Gentile attaches more importance to the purity of his caste than to matters of belief.

For the idolaters, Europeans were like pariahs, their lowest caste. These commit the gravest sin of eating cow's flesh. The idolaters believe that to convert to Christianity is to adopt the habits of the *farangi*s and thus lose your caste. That is a fate infinitely worse than

of a European gentleman who is degraded and loses his nobility. The
European, if he is wealthy, can still form alliances with respectable
members of his society, such as a rich merchant. An idolater who is
deprived of his caste can no longer be received in a respectable home
or find a husband for his daughter. He will have to either renounce
marriage alliances for his children or take for them pariah spouses.

Once the reverend fathers became aware of the Gentile aversion
towards the *farangi*, they tried to persuade them that they were not
*farangi*s but Roman Brahmins, Romapuris. Even today, when they are
sent to distant missions in the interior, the Jesuits dress and live after
the manner of Brahmins. A Jesuit demonstrates more repugnance
on being called a *farangi* than even a fair-skinned Gentile who is
mistakenly presumed to be one. In their mission of conversion, they
pander to Gentile caste prejudices and Gentile notions of who is high-
born and who is low-born. Father Malpica narrated that once, when
he was attending a service at a newly built church in the interior of
Goa, he was surprised to hear the priest extolling the noble birth of
our Saviour thus, 'Jesus was the king of all kings. His father's treasury
overflowed with so much gold that even the god Kuber was envious
of his wealth. The magnificence of his palace, the splendour of his
court, have never been matched, not even by the emperor Shah Jahan.'

When at the end of the service, Father Malpica confronted him
with falsifying the basic tenets of our faith, he was frank in his reply.
'Senor, do you think any Gentile would ever become a Christian if he
thought that the founder of our faith was so low-born as to grow up
in the household of a carpenter?'

The missionary efforts in the case of Mohammedans were even
less successful. I speak the language of experience when I say that
whatever progress may have been made by the missionaries among
the idolaters, by promises and alms as much as by preaching, they
would be disappointed if they supposed that in ten years even one
Mohammedan would agree to be converted to Christianity. It is true
that Mohammedans respect the religion of the New Testament: they
never speak of Jesus Christ but with great veneration, or pronounce

the name Isa, referring to Jesus, without adding the prefix 'Hazrat', Majesty. Like us, they even believe that Jesus was miraculously begotten and born of a virgin mother, and speak of him as 'Kalam-Allah' and 'Ruh-Allah'—the word of God and spirit of God. To hope, however, that they will renounce the religion wherein they were born, or be persuaded that Mohammed was a false prophet, is a mistake.

The Jesuits may have been naïve in their hopes, but they were clear-sighted and acute in their observations of the land and its peoples. They were unanimous in their opinion that we who lived in the capital city had no idea of the sufferings of the common people of the Indies, largely the idolaters. The land in its entirety belonged to the emperor and he granted to military officers a certain quantity of its produce in lieu of their wages. Similar grants were made to governors as their salary and for the upkeep of their troops, on condition that a portion of the surplus revenue yielded by the land was given to the king. The remaining royal lands were leased out to contractors on rent. The persons who had possession of the land had absolute authority over the peasants as also over the artisans and merchants of the towns and villages within their domain, and nothing could be more oppressive and cruel than the manner in which this authority was exercised. The cudgel and the kora compelled the people to do incessant labour for the benefit of these tyrants, a tyranny that drove the cultivator of the soil from his wretched home to a neighbouring state in the hope of finding milder treatment or to the army as the servant of some trooper. The Moguls, however, protested that the condition of idolaters could not be compared to the hardier and self-respecting peasants of Turkey or Persia, and that the sympathies of the Jesuits were misplaced; the Indians were a servile race, they said, and called them 'zulm-parast', tyranny-adorers. 'Yet the wish for justice remains alive in the most abject of human beings,' Father Malpica said. 'Look at the regard in which the Gentiles hold the emperor even when they know he is not well inclined towards their race.'

More than the crushing of rebellions within the empire and the conquests that considerably extended its frontiers, more than the magnificence of the Taj Mahal he built in the memory of his beloved wife who bore him fourteen children (the number of children and the manner of her death—in childbirth—is regarded by Indians as a proof of his enduring love), it was Emperor Shah Jahan's passion for justice that the common people talked about when they spoke of him as a great king. This did not stop many of them from irreverently arguing that this passion did not spring from deep belief but was based on eminently practical considerations. They said that a strict enforcement of laws that strikes terror in the hearts of both evildoers and those responsible for their apprehension and chastisement ensures that the emperor can spend more time in his harem. It relieved him of many cares of governance and allowed him the leisure to follow the real dictates of his heart, and his loins. They said this with an indulgent smile, however. A king may not be judged by his character but only by his effectiveness; more than other men, a king is a tree that should be judged by its fruits rather than its roots.

When an Indian acquires wealth, as is sometimes the case, he tends to acquaint himself with ways of appearing indigent—in his dress, lodgings or pleasures of the table—so as to avoid provoking the cupidity of the governor and his officers. If a person is at the receiving end of an injustice, there is no one before whom the oppressed peasant, artisan or trader can pour out his just complaints; the *kadis*, or magistrates, are not invested with sufficient power to restrain the oppression of the mighty and redress the wrongs of these unhappy people. This abuse of authority may not be felt to the same degree near the capital cities of Delhi and Agra, or in the vicinity of large towns and seaports such as Surat where acts of gross injustice cannot be concealed from the imperial court. Their only hope of protection from oppression being the monarch, his reputation for justice becomes the primary criteria by which he is judged by the people.

The emperor enjoyed quite a reputation for delivering speedy justice and the strict enforcement of laws that did not discriminate between high and low. As M. Gassendi used to say—and I can confirm his observation from my personal experiences—a people may want more from a ruler but they do not expect any less. Each morning, petitions held up by people in the crowd that gathered in the common assembly hall, the Diwan-e-Aam, would be brought to the emperor by the court officials. The petition would be read in his hearing and the monarch would then examine the concerned persons himself, often redressing the wrongs of the aggrieved party on the spot. On another day of the week, he would spend two hours to hear in private the petitions of ten poor subjects, selected and presented to the emperor by one of the Omrah. On yet another fixed weekday, he scrupulously attended the justice chamber attached to the palace where the two principal *kadis* helped him deal with cases referred to the imperial tribunal by other courts of the empire.

There was indeed discrimination in favour of Mohammedans in the framing of laws, but in his administration of justice, Shah Jahan did not distinguish between his Mohammedan co-religionists and his Gentile subjects. Father Roth remembered a case in Delhi where a Mohammedan soldier kidnapped the slave girl of a heathen clerk. The idolater lodged a complaint with the local court. The soldier insisted the slave girl belonged to him, and the girl, who wanted to live with the soldier, corroborated his version. The clerk persisted in his demand for justice and the case was transferred to the imperial tribunal where the emperor decreed that he would give his judgement after a month, during which time the girl was to live in his seraglio. One day, on the pretext that he wanted to write, the emperor ordered the girl to pour a thimble full of water into the inkwell, which the girl did most dexterously, without spilling a single drop. This proved to the king that the girl belonged to the scribe and not the soldier. The girl was restored to the clerk and the soldier was subjected to whipping before being banished from the empire.

But the monarch's chastisement of wrongdoers was rarely so indulgent; his passion for justice accompanied a preoccupation with the refinements of punishment. A commander who showed cowardice on the battlefield or somehow failed in his duty was not only severely dealt with but also had to suffer the misfortune of sharing his fate with his wives and daughters. To disgrace the commander and frighten others, the king ordered that rats be placed in the trousers of the women in his household after the trouser cuffs had been tied tightly around the ankles. In the case of a major theft, the punishment was death while a minor one warranted that the thief be sold as a slave to one of the Pathan tribes across the Indus or exchanged for one of their dogs, which, like their masters, are as handsome as they are savage. If a thief was not caught and the stolen goods remained untraced, the officials in whose jurisdiction the theft had taken place, primarily the *kotwal*, or the chief of police, were forced to compensate the victim for his loss. This, of course, made the *kotwal* even more of an extortionist while taking bribes.

The emperor's severest retribution was reserved for officials who failed to administer impartial justice. Father Roth, who had been an eyewitness to the emperor's punishment of Delhi's *kotwal*, notorious for taking bribes, told a fascinating story. The *kotwal* had apparently been hauled to the emperor's court and after the chief *kadi* had pronounced him guilty, the monarch had called to the court official in charge of poisonous snakes to step forward.

'We do not wish to prolong his agony. Let him be bitten on his left hand by a cobra. Which one would you recommend?' he asked.

A short discussion followed. The emperor was knowledgeable about snakes, as he was about many other matters—even discounting the flattery of the Omrah, he was universally regarded as the greatest expert on gems in the empire—and the choice finally fell on the *cobra capello*, one of the most poisonous snakes on earth.

'How long will he last?' the emperor inquired.

'Not more than three quarters of an hour, O Refuge of the World,' the official replied.

The order was given and the poor *kotwal*, his face ashen with fright, a mewling sound issuing from his throat, was dragged towards the basket containing cobras. The emperor remained seated for the one hour it took the man to die. The last bubbles of froth were still escaping from the *kotwal*'s blue lips after his heart had stopped beating when the king ordered the corpse to be thrown out on the open ground in front of the justice chamber. Unprotected from crows, dogs and the rats that came out at night, it lay there for two days, its rotting flesh horribly gouged and gashed, before it was released for burial.

Emperor Shah Jahan was not particularly cruel as eastern potentates go, but like Babur, his great-great-grandfather and the founder of the dynasty, he too delighted in thinking up ever more innovative means of torturing his enemies or simple criminals. This becomes a challenge when your predecessors have already made use of most of the possibilities for maiming the human body. Consider the punishment of flaying. Kings who had come before Babur had flayed men alive, stuffed the skin with straw and hung it out in the public square to strike terror in their subjects and dissuade criminals from even contemplating nefarious activities. Babur refined the cruel act further by having the offender's skin cut downward from the neck in blade-like strips, which were allowed to droop. A halter was put on the bleeding body of the poor wretch who was then dragged forward so that he stumbled and fell over the strips of his own skin. And what can anyone add to the simple yet highly inventive 'Kettle of Gruel' act, a Mogul method of torture favoured by Emperor Shah Jahan, wherein the offender's skull is cut open and a heated iron ball thrown into it with a pair of tongs, causing the brain to boil? Initiating new means of torture required as much time and ingenuity as novel ways of pursuing refined pleasure, and the emperor is, in fact, said to have expressed regret at his creativity in inflicting pain being limited by past innovations.

Father Roth agreed with me that we were fortunate that we lived in Europe, where sovereigns may often be unjust but never barbaric. Father Buze was the only one among the priests who believed that the quickness with which justice was delivered in India and the wide latitude given to the *kadi* to determine the quantum of punishment, which resulted in many acts of compassion, were enviable features of the Mogul system.

'And M. Bernier,' he insisted, 'you must admit that when it comes to women, food and buildings, your own sovereign, the illustrious Sun King, has the same powerful lusts as Shah Jahan although he may be fractionally more discreet than the Great Mogul when it comes to sexual dalliances.'

I concede that in order to uphold the honour of our great sovereign, I held forth on the wonders of our Sun King's reign and attempted to prove how his subjects excel in industry and courage over all other nations of earth. Gargantuan appetites are the birthright of kings, I explained, indeed the glory of a monarch and our Sire surpasses all other princes of the world in this respect, as he does in others. Father Buze listened tolerantly but I could sense a sceptical smile struggling to break through his pursed lips. But, then, in spite of the ten years or more he had spent in the country, the priest had lost little of his initial enthusiasm about the Indies and remained a fervent partisan to all things Indian.

Delhi was no different from Paris or any other capital city in the world where social conversation often tended to gravitate towards a discussion of the characters, doings and escapades of members of the royal family and thus it was not only the emperor but also Dara Shukoh who was an object of our scrutiny. I had observed that Father Roth was not as enthusiastic about Dara as the others; Father Buze, of course, counted himself among the prince's intimate friends, sharing a rapport with him that was lubricated by their common fondness for a most delicious liquor made from Persian wine and rosewater flavoured with spices and aromatic herbs distilled in the prince's own household.

One evening, when Father Roth and I were dining alone, I told him about the fruit of my researches into Dara's writings. I was glad to hear Father Roth confirm my doubts about the prince.

'The sincerity of Dara's writings is not reflected in his life,' the priest said in his dry Teutonic manner. 'Although the prince professes to be a Sufi of the Qadiriya order, he ignores the self-discipline and physical renunciation the order prescribes as essential for a novice. He wears dazzling gold and silk robes, eats the tastiest meats and the best dishes the royal kitchen can prepare, drinks the choicest wines from Persia and proceeds to bend Sufi teachings to fit them to his indulgences.'

The priest then drew my attention to a passage in the *Risala* where Dara writes, 'Worldliness is the non-remembering of God. It does not consist either in dress, or in having sons and a wife.' His is the path of grace, he writes, not of exertion: 'In the discipline of the school to which the author belongs, contrary to the practices of other schools, there is no asceticism. Everything here is love and affection, pleasure and ease.'

'Little wonder that the young prince Aurangzeb is heard calling his elder brother a hypocrite,' Father Roth concluded.

When, on his return, I presented Danishmand Khan with my conclusions, he listened to me thoughtfully before complimenting me in lofty words. 'You have done wonderful work, my friend. You have a gift of seeing people without being dazzled by the outer surface they have spent so much time polishing and which can easily deflect the naïve eye. Soon, I may have a task for you that is even more important.' He then presented me with two pearl necklaces and a Persian dagger with a gold handle encrusted with sparkling emeralds of superior quality from the mines of Panna in the Deccan.

I would soon realize that the task the Agha had set me—of assessing Dara Shukoh's character from his writings—was not out of idle curiosity on his part. The emperor had not been keeping well for three weeks and the Omrah had begun to worry about the succession to the Mogul throne upon his death or incapacitation. I am now convinced that my evening conversations with the Jesuit fathers, which were dominated by discussions on the person of Emperor Shah Jahan, his merits and his faults, almost as if we were engaged in writing his obituary, arose from the same unspoken and unacknowledged impulse, an anxiety that had begun to radiate outwards from Delhi towards the far outposts of the empire. By the time the Agha asked me to leave for the Deccan on an urgent and secret mission to Aurangzeb, the people's worst fears seemed to be coming true.

'The present ailment was nothing more mysterious than a painful swelling of His Majesty's private parts'

NICCOLAO MANUCCI

BY EARLY SEPTEMBER, 1657, Delhi was in chaos. All too suddenly the emperor, who had kept indifferent health the whole of summer, fell seriously ill. In the space of but three hours he developed an unusually high fever and for the next four days was unable to pass a drop of urine. The rumour that he lay at death's door flew out of the ramparts of the fort and spread in all directions through the length and breadth of the empire with the speed of Pegasus.

For the four days and nights that the emperor lay prone and was unable to make a public appearance, the city was in turmoil. Small groups of people engaged in animated discussion at street corners broke up frequently to scatter and then gather again at different corners in new groups, exchanging more rumours. Some claimed the Great Mogul was dead, others that he had been poisoned by one of the princes. There was a ludicrous story going around that the Indian nobles at the court had attempted a coup to overthrow the Persian

Omrah and the emperor had been killed in the ensuing fight. Fearing disturbances in the streets, the shopkeepers shut their shops. There were rumours of bands of looters breaking into shops at night. Old men recounted their memories of the utter chaos in which the empire had been plunged for more than a year during the war of succession between Emperor Jehangir's sons.

'This is just the beginning,' they said, pleased at the attention people were paying to their tales.

My daily presence at Prince Dara's court gave me privileged knowledge of the events as they occurred and I was glad to reassure the nervous Jesuit fathers that although the situation was serious there was no immediate danger to the emperor's life.

I believe I am the only European who watched from such close proximity the drama that followed the emperor's illness and shook the mighty empire by its roots. The fraud Frenchman, M. Bernier, may claim to have been a witness to the events, but his perception is not as much flawed—although there are many errors—as it is superficial. Consider the matter of the emperor's illness, which was not mysterious even if it remains obscure in chronicles of Emperor Shah Jahan's reign. One can understand when native historians, hoping for rewards or fearing punishment from the emperor (or his descendants), are circumspect when it comes to delicate matters that can affect the sovereign's reputation. But there is no excuse except ignorance for M. Bernier's claim that the Great Mogul was seized by a 'disorder', the nature of which he finds unbecoming to describe.

M. Bernier is a learned man, far more than I. But it does his reputation, and his scholarship and learning, little good when he hints at the possession of exact knowledge in elegant French without ever revealing it. He may have been correct in his observations on the general nature of the monarch's illness, but his pronouncements carry a tone of moral condemnation more suitable to a missionary than to someone who professes the noble calling of a physician.

M. Bernier was but a short time at the Mogul court, compared to the years I have spent in the Indies, and it is not like I was attached to Prince Dara's palace all those years. I travelled constantly, holding honourable and lucrative positions at the courts of native princes. My knowledge of people and events in the Mogul empire is not from books or from passing conversations with the natives who served in my household. It is of an order that can only come from long immersion in the life of a country and its people. Mine is knowledge that is not of the head but of the heart.

Everyone in Hindustan knew that Emperor Shah Jahan was a man of remarkable sexual appetite. He saw no reason to control it even when his beloved queen Mumtaz Mahal was alive. Yes, he mourned her death in many ways (he even gave up the practice of plucking out grey hair from his beard), but renouncing the pleasures promised by women's bodies was not one of them. I do not say he neglected Mumtaz Mahal when she was alive. After all, she bore him fourteen children in eighteen years. But with the queen pregnant most of the time and the native belief that intercourse with a pregnant woman harms the foetus—'Its soft head can be dented by the knocks from the tip of a hard penis,' my friend Mukarram Khan, the emperor's personal physician had confided in me—Shah Jahan's sexual energy always sought other outlets.

Age seemed to have increased the emperor's sexual ardour in the same proportion as his physical vigour had declined. At sixty-five years of age, yet reluctant to let go of his youth, the old monarch spent more and more time in his harem and, in desperation, sought to redress the mismatch through artifice. Not only did he apply a variety of drugs and unguents procured from all parts of India and beyond on his genitals, but if the stories of palace insiders were to be believed he had also commanded the construction of a large hall in his harem, twenty cubits in length and eight cubits wide, its walls and ceiling covered with large mirrors where the emperor could observe himself sporting with women.

Nor was there a limit to the number and variety of women he bedded. Not content with the two thousand queens, concubines, dancing girls, female musicians and slaves in his harem (although I admit that such a large figure serves more as an insignia of the emperor's power and majesty than the actual number of partners available to him for fornication), the emperor was also in the habit of inviting *kanjaris*, who traditionally visited the court on Wednesdays, to stay in the harem for a night to amuse him. These ravishing dancing girls were known for employing their amazingly supple limbs most innovatively in amorous sport, particularly (and I can personally vouch for their extraordinary skill) in tightening the muscles in their sex at will around the base of a man's shaft, affording him the most exquisite sensations, especially at the cusp of release. These girls, in fact, were so agile that when the emperor once wished to visit the Meena Bazaar, nine of them had apparently gathered in a clever formation to represent an elephant—four making the four feet, four others the body, and one the trunk—to enable his entry into the bazaar to be dramatic indeed. It had been heard that Shah Jahan often rode his 'elephant' in the privacy of his pleasure pavilion, both rider and elephant devoid of a stitch of clothing.

The emperor frequented Meena Bazaar often. Here, the wives and grown-up daughters of nobles played at being shopkeepers. Good-natured bargaining and playful banter often led to the extraction of promises of later, more private, meetings. Like other votaries of Venus, the licentious monarch dreaded the monotony that lurks at the edges of pleasure promised by women's bodies and found it necessary to add a hint of the illicit, a touch of danger, to his sexual encounters to keep boredom away. But, for one to whom nothing is forbidden, making sex dangerous proved to be a challenge and led him, at times, to overstep his bounds. In the rare instances when his advances were resisted, he simply used force to grab what was not freely granted. Most nobles at Emperor Shah Jahan's court were not less licentious than their liege, yet they were cautious not to interfere with the wives of other grandees. The emperor did not observe these restrictions.

In European countries love adventures only excite merriment and occasion witticisms and are then forgotten. But in India they are attached with dangers that cannot be imagined. More often than not, they are followed by some dreadful and tragic catastrophe. Indians, the Muslims in particular, zealously guard their women as the embodiment of their honour. I do not wish to pronounce a moral judgement when I speak of the emperor's sexual excesses. I am a man of flesh and blood myself, and in such matters I go by the dictum 'live and let live'. But I am of the firm opinion that the risks the emperor took in seducing the wives of his nobles were responsible to a great extent in eventually tearing apart an empire universally regarded as the most magnificent in Asia.

Emperor Shah Jahan's dalliances were many, but of these three affairs had the gravest consequences. The first and most notorious was his tryst with the wife of the captain-general of the imperial cavalry, Khalilullah Khan. The affair was so well known that insolent beggars harassed Khalilullah's wife as her litter was carried past them on the streets and addressed her tauntingly as 'Shah Jahan's lunch'.

On one occasion Emperor Shah Jahan had accused the hapless man in open court of embezzlement, an offence punishable by death. The emperor said he had heard that Khalilullah's wife wore shoes worth three million rupees and studded with precious stones. 'If your wife, of whose beauty we have heard much praise, wears such valuable shoes, then your wealth must be great indeed,' the emperor said, the menace in his voice highlighted by its apparent calm. 'It is evident that the greater part of this wealth must have been through embezzlement and the betrayal of the trust we have placed in you.'

Khalilullah had stood before the monarch with his head bowed, speechless at the allegation. His right hand involuntarily rose to rub his earlobe between a thumb and index finger. A stocky man with expressionless eyes, Khalilullah Khan had a thick growth of hair on his ear, like a bear's, about which he was extremely sensitive. The incessant manipulation of his earlobe whenever he was nervous was to check that no unruly hair had escaped the clipper.

The emperor's brother-in-law, Shaista Khan, a tall, barrel-chested man, who was prickly about all matters of honour, took the emperor's permission to reply on his behalf.

'Your Majesty,' he said. 'Khalilullah Khan's whole wealth is in those shoes. His wife has the habit of shoe-beating him on his face every morning. That is the only way he can enjoy his riches.'

Shaista Khan's intercession on his friend's behalf was not particularly witty. All the same, the emperor chuckled, which in turn gave the Omrah permission to break out in loud guffaws.

'To have such an angry wife at home is sufficient punishment,' the emperor said, dismissing the mortified wretch from his presence. Although he quietly swallowed the humiliation, Khalilullah never forgot the affront.

M. Bernier dishonestly spread quite a different version of the incident. It is the Wali Ahad, he reported, who used his shoes to beat Khalilullah. The man's wife finds no mention in his account of the incident. This is positively untrue. If what M. Bernier described were true, Khalilullah would have been so disgraced that he could neither have stayed on as commander of the imperial cavalry nor dared to show his face again at the court. Besides, Prince Dara, although partial to practical jokes, did not possess a mean or cruel streak. Rather, he was much given to laughter, and was generous to a fault.

The second of the emperor's widely known exploits involved Jafar Khan's wife, also known on the streets of Delhi as 'Shah Jahan's breakfast'. It is beyond dispute that Jafar Khan almost lost his life because of the emperor's passion for his wife. The Amir was saved only because his wife begged the emperor to spare his life and, instead, send him away to Patna as governor while she stayed back in Delhi. Jafar Khan, who valued his head above his honour, accepted the governorship with a show of effusive gratefulness. But did he forget the incident? Could he?

Perhaps the emperor's worst misstep was the rape of the wife of his brother-in-law, Shaista Khan. I do not believe the entire tale related to me by my friends in the imperial harem, but it is widely rumoured

that the virtuous noblewoman had been resisting the emperor's
propositions for a while, until one day, on Jahanara Begum's invitation,
she visited the palace for lunch. At the end of the feast, the emperor
joined the women. Once Princess Jahanara and the serving women had
left, he again importuned the lady, but finding her unwilling to accede
to his wishes, he raped her. On returning to her mansion, Shaista
Khan's wife refused to eat or change out of her torn shift. Within a
week, she died from grief. Her husband pretended to be ignorant of
what had taken place that day in the palace, but he silently vowed
vengeance. He was careful to hide the glow of revenge's fire that
had been lit in his heart that day, but the grave consequences of the
monarch's indulgences were to emerge soon enough.

India is not the only country where momentous events are too
often caused by insults to honour, or as a result of envy. Historians
ignore this truth and indulge in vain speculation as to the causes and
course of agitations that shake up empires. Like these historians,
M. Bernier too ignores the humanity of his actors and looks, instead,
to reasons of state and grand goals as causes for their actions. Any
observer of history, if he looks honestly and unsparingly at his own
life, will admit that it was steered less by reason than by passions of
which he often remained unaware. Why should they then believe that
princes are different? In my twenty years of close observation of Indian
potentates, I have been convinced that such passions sway powerful
monarchs even more than they do ordinary men. Doubtless, this holds
true for our European princes as well.

Am I being unfair to M. Bernier because of what happened
between us? In all honesty, no! I have many failings, but lack of honesty
is not one of them. M. Bernier is the type of European found in the
Indies who detests natives while being unfailingly polite to them.
He looks down upon his successful compatriots, such as I, if they are
low-born. M. Bernier is an honest man but one who is honest to his
pretensions, not to facts. He can only look at men and events through
the lens crafted by his upbringing and education. Nowhere does this
bias shine through more clearly than in his vain pronouncements the

characters of Prince Dara and that interloper Aurangzeb, the lead actors in the tragic drama that was soon to overtake the Mogul empire.

Nevertheless, the present ailment was nothing more mysterious than a painful swelling of His Majesty's private parts. Contrary to the stories that later did the rounds, it was not the consumption of shink, the spawn of a crocodile from the marshes of Lower Egypt, that almost killed the monarch. The truth is more prosaic. I have it on authority of Mukarram Khan that it was an overdose of a powder made from the crushed wings of a beetle found in Spain which led to this grievous outcome.

By the grace of God, the emperor survived the crisis. No one who witnessed the Wali Ahad's devoted caring of his father, when the emperor was given up for dead by even the most experienced hakims, can ever doubt the depth of the prince's filial love. Through the days and nights that the high fever burnt the emperor's brows and prevented him from opening his eyes, the prince rarely closed his own. At night, he rested on a carpet next to his father's bed and started at the least unrest the emperor displayed, his ears attuned to every sound like a mother's to the slightest mewl of distress from her baby.

Here, I must mention my own contribution, though a minor one, to the emperor's recovery. Hakim Tabinda, one of his attending physicians and a friend, was genuinely interested in Hindu medicine and often asked my opinion on how my teacher in Goa would treat a particular malady. One morning, just as I had woken up, he burst into my house in high agitation, his untied *qaba* flapping like a sail in high wind.

'Manucci, I have had a most powerful dream! It has left me quite shaken. In the dream I saw the emperor talking to Jahanara Begum on the medicinal virtues of the basil plant. Then the emperor turned to me, patted me on the cheek and said that his recovery began the day he took a broth made from its leaves. What do you know about these leaves?'

'Well, basil or tulsi, as the Hindus call it, is highly esteemed in their medicine. It is even considered sacred because of its miraculous qualities. My teacher used to call it the "elixir of life". He told me that in case of acute fevers, a decoction of its leaves boiled with powdered cardamom in half a litre of water and mixed with wild honey brings down the temperature,' I said.

It later reached my ears that when the Wali Ahad had heard how much the Hindus regarded the tulsi, and that its powers had been revealed to Tabinda in a dream, he commanded that the treatment be started immediately. Within twelve hours, the emperor's condition took a turn for the better.

Soon after his recovery, although he was still in fragile health, the emperor insisted on making a public appearance. More than the rumours about his death or incapacitation, he was disturbed by the news that his remaining three sons, Murad Baksh, Aurangzeb and Shah Shuja, acting in concert, were intent on marching to Delhi with the armies they had raised in their distant provinces. The vile Aurangzeb had persuaded them to adopt the stratagem of being loyal sons who were charging to rescue their father from captivity in the hands of their tyrannical brother, Dara. But there was no doubt in anybody's mind, least of all the emperor's, that the princes' only concern was ascending the throne. But the monarch had convinced himself that once he had attended court and shown that he was in full control, the rumours of his incapacity would be deprived of further fuel and the rebellious sons would return to their provinces. No one could dissuade him from this line of thought. Solicitous about his father's health, Prince Dara pleaded that the emperor at least keep the durbar small so as not to tax his energy.

On the evening of the twelfth of September 1657, forty of the highest-ranking Omrah, rajas, the ambassador of Persia and members of Prince Dara's retinue were summoned to attend the imperial court.

This was not my first glimpse of a court that was universally believed to be the most splendid in the world. Europeans who are in a position to compare and have no reason to exaggerate, say that, perhaps, with the exception of the Emperor of China, no other sovereign, not the King of Spain nor of France, not even the Sultan of Turkey, could match the magnificence of Emperor Shah Jahan's court.

The first time I had been presented at the court I was open-mouthed with wonder that human beings could create such grandeur and such pageantry. This evening, though, the opulence of the court's furnishings could not prevail our impoverished spirits. The brocade-draped pillars of the hall and carpets of the richest silk covering the floor lacked their usual sheen. The gold railing separating the balcony on which the Peacock Throne stood did not glow in the light of the jewelled candelabras. Even the magnificence of the throne, more a divan than a chair, which had on every previous occasion transfixed me with its six massive legs of gold studded with precious stones looked tawdry today. The two peacocks atop each column, thickset with gems and a tree set with rubies, emeralds, diamonds and pearls between them did not overwhelm me with their exquisite workmanship as they had done before. All I saw was a shrunken figure sitting cross-legged on a cushion, lost in the vastness of the throne. The turban of woven gold with an aigrette whose base was composed of large diamonds and one of the biggest topazes I had ever seen, seemed too heavy for the emperor's head. It kept slipping to one side, exposing the balding pate below. The necklace of immense pearls reaching down to his stomach could not mask the diminishing of authority that had taken place over the last ten days. When a sudden gust of wind made the chandeliers sway in long arcs, their wavering light making the pockmarks on his face stand out sharply against his papery skin, I realized with a start that the Great Mogul had been reduced to being just a shrivelled old man.

When the emperor spoke, however, his voice was firm, quite belying the fragility of his frame. He thanked the Almighty and asked the Wali Ahad to step forward.

'The prince Dara Shukoh has always shown infinitely more respect and affection for his father than my other sons. He has nursed his father to the utmost limit of possibility and that is the best form of worship of Allah. I desire that from today all the assembled and absent Omrah, and all the chief officers of the state, obey Prince Dara Shukoh as their sovereign in every matter, at all times and in every place.'

He proceeded to announce an increase of the prince's *mansab* by fifty thousand zat and an *inam* of two and a half lakh rupees. Then, turning to the prince, the emperor asked him to take his place on the Peacock Throne. 'If Allah prolongs my life for some days,' he said, 'I would desire to see my son Dara Shukoh in peaceable possession of the empire.'

Prince Dara, an emotional man at the best of times, was visibly moved. He did not proceed to the throne. Instead, bowing low before his father, he said, 'I pray for the long life of Your Majesty. While Allah preserves it, I cannot dream of ascending the throne, but will consider myself fortunate in being your humblest subject.'

A murmur of '*Alhamd-u-Lillah*', 'All praise and thanks be to Allah', rose from the assembled Omrah as they came forward, strictly in order of rank and seniority, to pay their homage to the Wali Ahad and renew their oath of fealty to the emperor. As one Amir after another made his low salaam and retreated, I wished I could read their impassive faces to uncover the secrets of their hearts. All the Omrah were apprehensive about the future, but it was impossible to identify the ones who were planning their acts of treachery and had shifted their loyalty to one or the other of Prince Dara's three brothers.

Even the display of fireworks on the bank of the Jamuna that night failed to dispel the anxiety that had gripped the imperial capital for almost a week. In other ways, too, the durbar did not quite have its intended effect. It may have brought a degree of calm to Delhi, but it further steeled the resolve of the three rebel princes to make an armed bid for the throne.

My sole refuge from politics and the crisis that gripped the empire was the house of the Jesuit fathers. M. Bernier, I heard, had been sent to the Deccan on some errand by his employer. I could thus freely visit the priests without running the risk of encountering that lying Frenchman. Another man of French origin, a more convivial companion than M. Bernier could ever hope to be, sometimes joined us. He was the executor of the two magnificent jewelled peacocks that adorned the imperial throne.

I was glad to contribute the bottles of excellent liquor Prince Dara had sent my way to our evenings of drinking and amiable chatter. Like all exiles, our talk was laced with nostalgia that became more intense as the evening wore on and the wine took effect. Once in a while, we returned to the current situation in India. The fathers agreed that Aurangzeb's victory in the coming struggle would spell an end to Jesuit missionary activities in India. They wanted Prince Dara to prevail, or even Shuja or Murad, but were not sanguine about their prospects.

Father Roth, who had been lately suffering from dyspepsia, summarized their feeling succinctly, 'Hindus have a saying, "*Yatha raja tatha praja* (As is the king, so are the subjects)". The truth is exactly the opposite. It is the king who is a reflection of his people. If the people are dishonest, the king is even more corrupt. He is a tyrant if the people he rules are violent. Indians are a malicious, scheming lot. Their monarch can only be someone as malevolent as Aurangzeb; Dara is too good-hearted.'

One of the first indications that the inevitable war, though as yet undeclared, was upon Hindustan occurred very soon after the emperor's miraculous recovery.

One evening, I had just finished dinner when a man in the Wali Ahad's service came with a message that I was to proceed immediately to Princess Jahanara's apartments in the imperial palace. As soon as I entered the waiting carriage, it set off at a great speed towards the Royal Square. The messenger was unable to tell me the nature of the emergency. I gauged the seriousness of the situation when I observed upon my arrival that all the rules governing entry into the harem had been suspended. I found myself waiting in the antechamber of Princess Jahanara's apartment with at least ten other doctors who were engaged in discussions in hushed whispers.

It appeared that the princess had taken ill in the morning with symptoms of acute poisoning. The emperor, the Wali Ahad and Mukarram Khan were with her in the bedroom. The doctors waiting outside were being summoned inside, one by one, for their opinion. When a doctor emerged, the others would surround him, eager for the latest tidings. We were told that the distraught emperor was just sitting in a chair, muttering a prayer. His eyes were closed, his palms supporting his bowed head, as he beseeched the Almighty to spare his daughter's life in a low mumble. Prince Dara was pacing around the room, often stopping to look at his sister lying motionless in the bed, her face fast losing colour. 'Can't you do something? Do something!' he would sometimes angrily command the conferring doctors.

I became more and more concerned as I heard that the princess's condition was deteriorating. I am not one who is given to fulsomeness in my expression, but the few times that I had had the privilege of being called upon to bleed the princess, I had found her to be a rare combination of beauty and intellect. Rarer still was the existence of these attributes alongside a loving heart full of generosity and compassion that did not distinguish between the status of its recipients. As far as I had heard, she was as helpful in furthering the forbidden liaison of an attending maid who had fallen in love with a Hindu scribe as she was in interceding with her father to save the king of Golconda from a ruinous war Aurangzeb was attempting to foist on the Deccan kingdom.

I am not ashamed to admit that I had always looked forward to our bloodletting sessions.

'Ah, my handsome Niccolao is here,' Jahanara Begum would sing out to her attendants. 'He is like a vampire, this *farangi*, always on the lookout to suck some blood from my weak body. Look, how red his lips have become!'

Red, though, was nearer the colour of my ears than my lips as she laughed at my evident embarrassment, thereby heightening it.

I would watch as one mesmerized as the beautiful princess rolled up the sleeve of her tunic and extended a slim, alabaster-white forearm towards me. I could feel her eyes on me as I stroked the selected spot for just a little longer than was necessary. When, unable to resist, I would raise my eyes to meet her level gaze, I could never resist the laughter in her soot-black eyes shaded by thick lashes and framed by thin eyebrows the shape of perfect scimitars. More often than not, I would have to avert my gaze quickly as I felt my ears grow hot and the blood rush to my cheeks. At these times the princess was gracious enough to divert me by asking me about Venice and my journey across the seas to India.

'Ah, Niccolao, do not form an opinion of the princess based on her outer shell alone,' Father Buze said when I told him wistfully of my visits to the princess's palace. 'There has been no woman in the history of the House of Timur who was so beautiful, accomplished and universally loved as she is. Do you know that Mullah Shah has initiated her into the Sufi order of the Chistis even though she is a woman? He holds such a high opinion of her spiritual gifts that he once publicly announced in Prince Dara's court that her mystical knowledge being as extraordinary as it is, he considers her worthy of being his representative. Let me show you something.'

From his room, Father Buze brought out a slim book bound in burnished calf leather.

'This is her book, *Munis-ul-Arwah*, a biography of the founder of her Order, in which she has described some of her own experiences,' he remarked as he opened it to a page which had its upper corner turned down.

He began to translate it laboriously: 'I seated myself in a corner with my face turned towards Mecca, and concentrated all my mind on the image of the Master, calling up at the same time, in my imagination, my vision of the most holy Prophet. Occupied with this contemplation, I arrived at a state of my soul in which I neither slept nor was awake. And then I saw the holy company of the Prophet and his four friends. I also saw Mullah Shah. He was seated beside the Prophet, upon whose feet his head lay, while the Prophet said to him, "O Mullah Shah, for what reason did you illumine that Timuri?"

Praise be to Allah who, through the particular attention of the holy Master, has accorded to me, a poor woman, the gift of conceiving the Supreme Being in the most complete manner, as I have always desired. Every man who has attained this supreme felicity becomes through this fact the most accomplished and the most noble of beings. His individual existence vanishes in Absolute Existence. He becomes a drop in the ocean, a mote in the sunshine, an atom in the totality. Arrived in this state, he is above death, future punishment, the Garden of Paradise and the Fire of Hell. Whether man or woman, he is always the most Perfect Being.'

I had listened attentively but found it difficult to reconcile the two images: the laughing, beautiful woman flushed with sensuality on the one hand and the lofty mystic absorbed in contemplation of God on the other. Jahanara Begum loved Prince Dara more than her other brothers and often influenced her father on his behalf not only because he was a brother in flesh but also in spirit, a fellow seeker of truth.

I have heard from various quarters that M. Bernier has maligned the princess by calling her promiscuous and has even gone so far as to repeat with conviction the bazaar gossip that she was her father's mistress. Yes, her father loved her, as did everyone else, but his love was that of a father for a daughter, not a lover for his beloved. There had indeed been talk of her liaison with a handsome young man of no exalted rank, whom the emperor forbade her from marrying, but the crass Frenchman has provided his listeners with absurd details of some imagined tale. According to M. Bernier, the emperor surprised the lovers by entering the harem at an unusual hour, causing the gallant to hide himself in a capacious cauldron used for baths. Having guessed where he was hiding, the cunning emperor told his daughter in the course of their conversation that her normally clear skin looked smudged. She needed a bath, he decreed, and instructed the eunuchs to light a fire under the cauldron. He continued to talk to the distraught princess, seemingly oblivious to the shrieks coming from inside the cauldron, and only retired when the eunuchs, who were holding down the lid, gave him to understand that the man inside was dead. I am not sure how people have believed such a sorry tale. If the emperor withheld his permission for her marriage, he was simply following the rule made by his grandfather Akbar that a royal princess should not be given in marriage because her husband, in becoming powerful through the royal alliance, may himself aspire to the throne.

M. Bernier has circulated another piece of gossip as gospel truth. Once, on suspicion of illicit relations between his daughter and a young nobleman, he says, the emperor presented the unsuspecting youth with a paan as a special mark of royal favour. According to custom, the young man was obliged to immediately chew on the paan while expressing gratefulness for the signal honour, and he died from the poison in the paan before he could reach home. I leave it to readers to judge whether a man who loved his daughter so much would cause her such grievous harm. And that too under the scrutiny of an entire court where there were so many nobles and ambassadors who would be witness to the emperor's viciousness!

Jahanara Begum undoubtedly had lovers, but the emperor ignored their existence as long as she was discreet. As the first lady of the empire, she did not need to hide herself from men who had cause to visit the imperial harem.

In this hour of her need, I wished that I had studied medicine in the more formal setting of a university, that I knew more about poisons and their antidotes, and was not limited by the specialized knowledge I had acquired at the Royal Hospital in Goa or from Vaidraj.

The symptoms the princess had displayed—abdominal pain, diarrhoea and vomiting—being indistinguishable from a severe stomach upset had been initially treated as such. Only after an alert slave girl informed the attending physician that the princess had been on a fast the entire day, as part of her spiritual regimen, was poison suspected.

Everyone was at a loss: If the princess had not eaten a morsel the whole day, how had she ingested the poison? In the end, it was left to Khwaja Younis, the chief eunuch of Prince Dara's harem, to solve the mystery. Khwaja Younis commanded the slave girls to reconstruct a minute by minute account of the princess's activities through the day. The attendants, still shaking and distraught, filled in bits of the puzzle. It transpired that in the early hours of the morning, the princess had received a book penned in the finest calligraphic hand, each page outlined in striking, decorative borders. In her eagerness to read the book, Jahanara Begum immediately opened it, but finding the first five pages stuck together she proceeded to separate them by repeatedly wetting the index finger of her right hand with her spittle and sliding it across the page that was stuck to the one below. It became clear that this was how the poison had entered her stomach: the pages were glued together with a paste made from castor beans, a deadly poison that mimics the symptoms of stomach cramps.

No one knew who had sent the book—it had been handed to a guard by a well-dressed stranger—but in our minds there was little doubt that the attempt to poison the princess was the fiend Aurangzeb's handiwork. I could not fathom the evil in a brother's hearts that would prompt him to go to such lengths to harm such a sister. We have since been proved right as the younger prince's preference for poison as a tool of assassination is now acknowledged by everyone except his blatant partisans.

'In his unguarded moments he called Aurangzeb "the white snake"'

FRANCOIS BERNIER

I BELIEVE THAT OVER the years I have developed and refined my skills in judging a person's character, guided chiefly by M. Gassendi's advice to mistrust first impressions and wait for my mind to form a considered opinion rather than grasping at one in haste. I was thus disheartened to observe Danishmand Khan, whom I had always considered a picture of equanimity, unmoved by the storms swirling around him, become as anxious and restless as he did in the days following the emperor's illness in the beginning of September 1657.

From what we heard, the illness was serious, brought about by an excess of priapism highly unbecoming a man who had crossed the age of sixty.

'Men deal with the loss of love differently, Bernier,' the Agha chided me for my expression of disapproval. 'Some will never again plant a garden of love around them once the old one has withered. Others, like our monarch—and never doubt that he loved Mumtaz Mahal dearly— seem to go berserk in their consumption of female flesh. Their erotic *junoon*, delirium if I may call it so, however, is but an attempt to relieve a pain that is only fleetingly assuaged in the moment of an embrace before it returns with its original severity. What I worry about is that if the emperor does not recover in the next few days, it may be too late to save the empire from the ill fortune that is already knocking at its door. Perhaps it is too late already. Once the rumour reaches the princes that the emperor is dying—even though he is alive—the war of succession will become inevitable. With all the upheavals in the House of Timur over the last two centuries, I am no longer confident that its foundations are strong enough to withstand any further buffets.'

In the absence of reliable news about the emperor's illness, there were indeed all kinds of rumours circulating in the bazaars of Delhi. 'The emperor is already dead', 'The princes, Aurangzeb, Murad and Shuja, are marching their armies to Delhi' were the most rampant among these. As the anxiety at the looming violence had become palpable, so had the excitement at hearing the waves of fresh rumours, which seemed to breathe fresh life into normal, everyday life. I was frequently amused to see Khwaja Chisti's mien assume a strange gravity as he conveyed a rumour, quite unlike the mischievous glee that always accompanied his relay of its sibling, a piece of gossip.

'All we know for certain from my sources in the palace, Bernier,' the Agha told me on the evening of the tenth day of September, his face drawn with worry, is that for four days, the emperor has had high fever and is lying motionless except for an occasional mysterious effort to lift a hand to his nose. Jahanara Begum has been tending to her sick father day and night. With the exception of Jahanara Begum, the Wali Ahad, the chief hakim, and the emperor's personal retainers, no one else has been allowed to see him during this time. All the gates of the Red Fort except for two have been closed and these are guarded by Raja Jaswant Singh of Marwar and Raja Ram Singh of Kishangarh with their thirty thousand Rajput soldiers.'

On the way out of the Agha's chambers, Khwaja Chisti, who was accompanying me, said quietly, 'Bernier, there is much more going on under the surface than the Agha knows. Whenever I try to tell him, he rebukes me severely. He thinks I am repeating rumours I have heard on the streets. But my information is reliable. It comes from my best friend Niamat, who may be out of favour with the emperor now, but once personally served him and still has good contacts in the palace. Why have all the Mohammedan commanders been removed from guard duty? Is it the emperor or some other high personage who doesn't trust them?'

Chisti gave me a meaningful look before continuing. 'Niamat tells me that Jahanara Begum is the only person allowed to be in the emperor's bed chamber. Prince Dara is permitted entry into the fort only during the day. I tell you the monarch is on his death bed, poisoned by the same high personage who holds him prisoner.'

Chisti's dire forecast about the emperor's imminent demise, however, proved unfounded, since four days later we heard that the emperor was feeling better and would make an appearance before the populace through a window of his chamber in the palace. As it happened, the emaciated figure that appeared at the window for a few seconds failed to convince most onlookers; many believed the figure was merely an impostor, an old eunuch dressed in imperial robes, and that Dara had indeed imprisoned his father, or perhaps even killed him. I do not know if Aurangzeb, Murad and Shuja really believed the rumours or only pretended to believe them.

The Agha's house witnessed a flood of visitors during those days: Omrah and Hindu rajas seeking information, or the Agha's opinions, on the looming crisis; and messengers from Gujarat, Bengal and the Deccan bringing the latest tidings from the courts of the three princes. The news was ominous, though not unexpected; the brothers were rushing to raise large armies to march to Delhi and make their claim for the throne of the Indies.

Most Omrah wanted to know whether Danishmand Khan was already committed to the cause of one or the other prince in the war of succession, which seemed to become inevitable in the absence of any signs of the emperor's recovery as the days went by. They believed that as the foreign minister the Agha exercised some influence at the courts of Persia and Balkh and could persuade one or the other sovereign to intervene on behalf of the prince he favoured as successor to the Great Mogul. Jafar Khan was a frequent visitor at the beginning of the crisis, urging the Agha to quickly commit himself to Aurangzeb's side if he wanted to reap the rewards from the coming dispensation, but his visits soon tapered off as he threw himself into the vortex of the fast-moving events.

The Agha was an honourable man who had sworn an oath of fealty to the emperor. Every day he agonized over the question of his loyalty: was his oath bound to the person of the emperor or to what he represented, the sanctity and welfare of the empire? A diplomat by temperament and long practice, he could not discuss his mental turmoil with other nobles, each of them by now scampering to find shelter from the coming storm—and thus, by default, I became his confidant. He would send for me in the late evenings when the last of his visitors had left; the only demand on me was to listen without interrupting or offering my opinion.

A few weeks later the Agha told me that the emperor had left for Agra. 'He is proud of the new capital he has built in Delhi but his heart lies in Agra, where Mumtaz Mahal is buried. From the windows of his bed chamber in the Agra fort, he can see her tomb and relive the memories of their years together.'

I did not have to enquire further to know that the emperor's recovery was now of little consequence, since the princes' ambitions had set into motion events that were now irreversible.

'The fresh reports I receive every day indicate that the princes will not be dissuaded in their preparations for war by court dispatches under the emperor's seal,' the Agha was saying. 'They dismiss these as forgeries . . .' As he spoke, I gradually understood that the Agha's dilemma in choosing between the princes Dara and Aurangzeb—Shuja and Murad never even entered his mind—involved not just the moral and political aspects of kingship but also personal considerations that troubled him even though he was determined to disregard their impact on his choice.

Danishmand Khan had known both the princes intimately as boys from the time when the boys' grandfather, Emperor Jahangir, ruled the kingdom and Emperor Shah Jahan, or Prince Khurram as he was then called, was the viceroy of the Deccan. Intoxicated by the military successes of the previous years, when he had forced the Sultans of Bijapur and Ahmednagar to acknowledge Mogul suzerainty, Prince Khurram had already set his sights on the imperial throne. He had attacked Agra when his father was on his way to Kashmir for the summer but had been left frustrated by the city's outstanding defences. Then, in a pitched battle near Delhi, the prince had been decisively defeated by the imperial army and was forced to flee to the south and take refuge in the very kingdoms he had left as a victor on an ill-fated venture to overthrow his father. The final terms of his surrender included the transfer of his sons, Dara, who was ten years old at the time, and Aurangzeb, who was six, as hostages to the imperial court, and Danishmand Khan had been entrusted with the responsibility of the princes' education and accompanied the boys to Lahore where they were to stay for the next three years.

'How different the two boys were, Bernier!' the Agha reminisced. 'Both received the same education as any other Mughal prince: lessons on the Holy Quran, the history of the house of Timur and Persian poetry. Dara and Aurangzeb were both conscientious students and diligent in completing their assignments, but it was evident that Aurangzeb did not share Dara's love for poetry. Not only was he indifferent to the music of poetry but he also considered it a waste of time. He would rather spend hours studying the Holy Book.'

We were sitting in the pavilion in the Agha's garden, inhaling the soft scent of jasmine and roses. The idolater festival that marks the onset of winter was no more than two weeks away and the evenings had become cool. A single servant stood at a discreet distance in the shadows thrown by lit torches that dotted the garden. Another now approached us carrying fresh hukkas. I had developed a taste for tobacco, pleased that the Agha had invited me to smoke in his company; it was the ultimate mark of his favour.

'I remember a hunt for tigers near Lahore, on which I had accompanied the emperor and the princes. Tigers are plentiful in the jungles bordering the road to Delhi. All the preparations had been made. A stretch of the jungle where the animals had been sighted was identified for the royal hunt. In the preceding three days, cows, buffaloes and goats had been pushed into this part of the jungle so that the tigers did not migrate to other areas. On the morning of the hunt, the jungle was encircled with high nets, with only one opening through which the royal hunting party could enter. Soldiers stood around the net, more to scare the tigers towards the hunters than to wound or kill them.

'It was around eleven in the morning and the winter fog had just begun to lift when we entered the jungle. Emperor Jahangir had once again overindulged on alcohol and was sleeping off·the effects of his excesses. The empress Nurjahan, the boys' grandmother, sat in an uncovered howdah on the first elephant. She was a beautiful woman, Bernier, surpassing even the comeliness of Princess Jahanara. I can still recall how she was dressed that day: tight grey silk breeches, a silk shirt and a long coat of the finest Kashmir wool embroidered with gold thread. A veil hung over her face from a long pointed cap studded with pearls and emeralds. Elephants carrying the princes and other nobles followed. Dara and Aurangzeb were with me somewhere in the middle of this procession of elephants trudging deeper into the jungle. Dara was like a twittering bird, his thin neck moving constantly from one side to the other as he sought to draw my attention to the plumage of unfamiliar birds or to the dexterous monkeys swinging on the branches overhead and barraged me with questions on natural history. Aurangzeb scarcely looked up. His attention was focussed on my matchlock. He was subjecting the weapon to minute scrutiny, determined to unearth the secrets of its working.

'The empress shot a tiger that day—her first. In the celebration that followed in the jungle itself, the brothers were each presented with a mini matchlock. Their reactions were typical. Dara barely gave the gun a glance, his attention still focussed on the birds and vegetation. Aurangzeb sat alone, far from the festivities, absorbed in the weapon.' I knew then that he was well on his way to what he has become as a man—an enemy of all graces.'

Danishmand Khan acknowledged that, by nature, Dara had been more attractive than his younger brother. Even as a boy, Aurangzeb's countenance had been composed at all times and his eyes were grave beyond his years. Not for him Dara's open-faced delight and the quick laughter that crinkled up the corners of his eyes, seductive to even those who had heard of the boy's easy charm and were determined to resist it. In contrast, Aurangzeb rarely smiled. And when he did, no one could be sure if it was merely a matter of courtesy, a calculated tribute demanded by the situation, rather than a spontaneous gesture. But even though rarely friendly, he was unfailingly polite. 'Aurangzeb knew early in life that politeness makes people pliable, that courtesy is to human nature as warmth is to wax,' the Agha said thoughtfully.

As his teacher, Danishmand Khan could sense Aurangzeb's hurry to flee from childhood and become a man. The man he glimpsed through the widening cracks in the eggshell of boyishness was confident and, above all, self-sufficient. He remembered that as a child Aurangzeb was quite content to be by himself, needing neither playmates nor adults for guidance or approval of his solitary activities. On the other hand, the older prince always needed an audience. 'Admiration of others was the sun that made Dara flower. And admiration was a nutrient the boy had in abundance. Not only because he was the heir to the throne and the undisputed favourite of his father but also because he was bright, gifted, handsome, open and very, very generous. But Allah's ways are unfathomable, Bernier, praised be the All-Merciful. He takes away with one hand and gives with the other. Allah saw it fit to compensate the younger child's pain of being pushed into the background and his enforced exile into silence with a boon that all good kings require: Aurangzeb developed a heightened sensibility for other people's wants even when the want was unarticulated. Dara, who received so much, was and remains indifferent to everyone's desires but his own.

'It did not help that Prince Khurram showed an open aversion to Aurangzeb when the boys were reunited with their parents. He observed the formalities of fatherhood well enough. Aurangzeb was always included in the party when, after he became emperor, Shah Jahan took the princes with him on a hunt or on a visit to a mosque. There was no discrimination in the celebration of the boy's birthday or in the value of presents Mughal tradition required the emperor to make to a prince. The emperor's aversion to his third son took subtler forms. His brows would knit, his lips would purse and eyes become glazed and expressionless when Aurangzeb was ushered into his presence, whether in the harem or in the court. One only had to contrast Aurangzeb's reception to the open delight with which Dara was greeted. Everyone could see the effort the emperor was making in not springing up from his seat and rushing to hug the boy and lift him up in his arms. To see your father's eyes light up when they look upon your brother and become opaque when you come into his presence would deeply affect any child. I know that Aurangzeb was a reserved boy, not shy but self-sufficient, and did not feel the need to reach out to others. Even I, his tutor, never knew what was really going on behind his closed visage and consistent courtesy.'

'Did something happen, Agha, that made the emperor dislike Aurangzeb so much? Or was it just that the boy was not personable?' I asked.

'Two incidents come to mind, Bernier. I was present at the first, the second I have heard of. The first incident took place two days before Aurangzeb's birth. Prince Khurram was returning with Emperor Jahangir from Gujarat to Agra and the imperial household had set up camp next to the village of Dohad on the border of Gujarat and Malwa. The next day, after the afternoon prayers, when the emperor, accompanied by Khurram and a few nobles—I was among them—visited the village to grant an audience to its inhabitants, an old heathen woman approached him.

'"My name is Nalini, Jahanpanah," she said, "and my profession is to read the lines of fate on the forehead."

'Intrigued, Jahangir motioned his bodyguards to let the woman pass. "Can you read fate's handwriting on the brow of my son, Prince Khurram?" he enquired.

'Like any other fortune-teller, the woman was cryptic in her communications, her words laden with layers of meaning, none of them obvious. Yet there was one prediction that was less obscure than others, which chilled the blood flowing through Khurram's heart. "The child who is in your wife's womb will be incomparably brave and fearless," she said. "Your destiny will rest in his hands. Remember, my prince, we begin to die at birth. The end flows from the beginning."'

The second incident the Agha recounted had occurred when, after his abortive rebellion, Prince Khurram's fortunes were at such a low ebb that not many would have predicted his eventual ascent to the Mogul throne as Emperor Shah Jahan. In fact, the prince was virtually a prisoner of the Sultan of Bijapur who had been asked by Emperor Jahangir to restrain him, by force if necessary, if he made a move to leave the kingdom. While in Bijapur, Mumtaz Mahal, who was again pregnant, expressed a wish to eat apples. Dejected at his circumstances, which did not permit him to satisfy such a minor whim, the prince left the house and went out on the street. Here he met a fakir who hailed him by his name and offered him two apples.

'You must be a holy man to know and fulfil what I crave for most at this moment,' Prince Khurram said humbly. 'Will you talk to me?'

The fakir nodded his assent and they had a long conversation. Among other things, the fakir told the prince that he would fall ill often and on such occasions he should smell his hands. 'If they smell of apples you will always recover, no matter how dangerous the illness appears to the doctors. But when the smell vanishes, even a common cold can be the vehicle of death.'

'And after my death, will any of my sons dim the glory of the Mughals, be the destroyer of our race?'

'It will be Aurangzeb,' the fakir had declared.

After this encounter, Prince Khurram found it difficult to hide his dislike for his son, then nine years old. In his unguarded moments he called Aurangzeb 'the white snake', referring to the boy's pale complexion. It reminded him of the pallor of a leper's skin, he would remark in the boy's hearing, his mouth wrinkling in distaste.

'But, even as a boy, Aurangzeb's self-control was exemplary,' Danishmand Khan said. 'I could only guess at the embers of rage that smouldered under the icy layer of hate that coated his heart.'

To his credit, Danishmand Khan did not for even a moment entertain the claims of the other princes, Murad and Shuja. As far as he was concerned, their abandonment to excessive and shameless luxury, their addiction to the vice of drunkenness, their unfeeling and brutal cruelty, had effectively taken them out of the race for the throne of the Indies. The Agha was scathing in his appraisal of Murad who spent most of his days absorbed in the pleasures of the chase and the table. He allowed that Murad was not unlike most Omrah, who can wax sentimental over a pack of dogs and lavish the beasts with attention and affection, while remaining utterly indifferent to the plight of the poor wretches who have to follow their master on foot through thorny bushes and thick scrub, in the burning heat of summer or on chilly winter mornings, in pursuit of game.

The Agha was convinced that many of the vices of the Mogul princes could be directly attributed to shortcomings in their early education. The princes grew up in the seraglio, which is organized around the pursuit of pleasure and even raises such pursuit to the status of being the highest goal in one's life. The Agha said that having witnessing their fathers indulging in drunken orgies from their earliest years, their care entrusted to women and eunuchs—slaves with the mentality of being servile to superiors and oppressive towards inferiors—it was remarkable that a few of the princes yet turned out to be wise and just sovereigns. To a large extent, such felicitous outcomes depended on the calibre of the teacher the emperor chose for the education of his sons. 'From the very beginning, my message to my young charges was that as you will surpass others in power and elevation, so must you be pre-eminent in virtue and knowledge. I was lucky that both Dara and Aurangzeb were receptive to this message.'

As he rummaged deeper into his memories, it was apparent to me that the Agha had made his up his mind about which prince he would support, but he still wished to throw light on it from every angle before he confided his decision to the few people he trusted. What weighed in on Dara's side was less the prince's likeability than Danishmand Khan's oath of loyalty to his emperor, which also implied obedience to his wishes. What inclined him in Aurangzeb's favour were some of the qualities he had observed in the prince since the latter was a child and which the Agha believed would make for a good, perhaps even a great emperor. These qualities were not only of the mind but also of his body: his physical fortitude, for instance.

'One evening in Lahore, in a fit of drunken rage, Emperor Jahangir had started slapping the boy. I forget the nature of his transgression. Something quite minor, I believe. He could not have been more than eight at the time. Aurangzeb bore his grandfather's beating without protest or even a whimper. Enraged at getting no reaction, the king hit the boy with redoubled fury till blood oozed from a cut lip and the side of his mouth. Yet Aurangzeb stood still, any expression of pain buried deep in his eyes, invisible to witnesses. Later, when the emperor had calmed down—or was again sober—he presented the boy with a necklace of Basra pearls and asked how it was that he had not reacted to the beating. "My teacher has told me that it is the greatest shame for a Mughal prince to cry when in pain," Aurangzeb replied.

'Dara's singular flaw is that he cannot hate and thus cannot summon enough energy and resolution to thwart his enemies since they do not exist in his mind but only in the world outside. And with the spiritual and philosophical cast to his mind, the outside world has never been as real to him as it is to the rest of us. In the absence of hate, Dara cannot recognize an enemy. Oh yes, he despises Aurangzeb; calls him a *namazi*, talks of him as 'more a prayer mat than a man', referring to his punctiliousness in the matter of carrying out the prescribed prayers. But has despising another ever given anyone as much energy as hating him? Aurangzeb can hate but *his* flaw is that he cannot stop hating. His enmities endure because he will never give his enemies a chance to become his friends. A truly great monarch, like their great-grandfather Akbar, must be able to hate but must also be able to control his hatred. Yet, how well Aurangzeb hides his feelings! He will not forget a slight but his face will never betray his true emotions.'

I was not surprised when at the end of his agonizing Danishmand Khan declared that he would align himself with Aurangzeb, choosing the well-being of the empire over the wishes of the emperor.

'Aurangzeb will extend the empire and keep it safe from external aggression and internal strife. Dara divides the Faithful. Aurangzeb will unite them. He will strengthen the empire's foundations so that, *insha'allah*, the Mughal dynasty will continue to rule Hindustan for centuries to come,' he said.

He announced his decision to send Imran Khan, his trusted secretary, as his emissary to Aurangzeb in the Deccan to assure the prince of his support and to convey that he would do his utmost to ensure that no foreign power, neither Persia nor Balkh, intervened on behalf of any other prince. He asked me if I would accompany Imran Khan. 'You will do me a great favour, my friend,' he said, 'if you will travel to Aurangzeb's camp and return with your personal impressions of him. People tell me that he has not changed at all and, if anything, has become more resolute in his undertakings.'

I answered that I would gladly embark on the mission in service of the Agha. Besides a closer look at Aurangzeb, it would also afford me an opportunity to travel and escape the oppressive confines of Delhi.

*'Thus are a man's noblest acts of love laid low
by the indifference of fate'*

NICCOLAO MANUCCI

I DO NOT WANT to give the false impression that I was present when Prince Dara and his advisers discussed the strategies to counter the plans of his brothers. I was part of the Wali Ahad's court, but not of the key circle. But there are no secrets in Indian courts, especially for one such as I, who had ministered to the harems of the prince's closest advisers and was on cordial terms with most of them. I was a small man, but I had big friends.

I must confess that the impending war had filled me with an unfamiliar sense of exhilaration. Like an approaching gale that spreads unrest among the trees in a forest, I could hear the sounds of war from afar: the heavy tread of the infantry to the flourish of kettle drums, the neighing of horses as trumpets were sounded, the roar of cannons shaking the sky. I wanted to be a part of it. War may be the trade of kings but everyone covets the merchandise. I could not stand aloof from the promise of a rush to glory, unable to envision that it could equally be a rush to the grave. My conviction that my star would help me ride out any storm remained unshaken.

All I had wanted when I set out for India was to become rich, live out my youth in a tropical villa in the willing company of beautiful women, and return to Venice in my old age where, flush with money, I would walk with my head high even if I did not belong to the ruling classes. Now I found myself thrilling to the advance of a war in a foreign land, a battle between brothers in which my personal stake was low indeed. The prospect of participating in the war produced a restiveness in my veins quite different from the one I experienced when I occasionally looked into the chest under my bed, now bulging with treasure. In some ways, I felt this urge more keenly than the times when I had lain with Mala or Maria.

At the court, news trickled in every day of the activities in the far-off provinces of Bengal, the Deccan and Gujarat, where Shuja, Aurangzeb and Murad prepared to make their bid for the imperial throne. Even though Prince Dara was impatient to act fast and foil his brothers' plans at the earliest, the emperor's reluctance to accept that the other princes had turned against their father held him back. With the convenient memory of old age, the monarch had erased all recollection of his own rebellion against his father and the murder of his brother and rival to the throne, Shahryar, carried out under his orders. He insisted that his sons, isolated as they were from their father and from Delhi in their distant posts, had been misinformed about the severity of his illness and that their concern for his health was leading them to take unwise action. Perhaps I, too, should be less harsh in judging the emperor as a foolish and stubborn old man. It is an unfortunate fact that parents love their children more than they are loved in return. As humans, we are deeply moved when we listen to songs of legendary lovers bemoaning the loss or the turning away of their beloved, but often remain oblivious to the mute, unrequited love of countless fathers and mothers.

Although still ailing and weak, the monarch decided to leave Delhi for Agra, a distance of sixty-six leagues. After a week, the Wali Ahad's court followed suit. Emperor Shah Jahan was convinced that when people saw him and his train on the road, the news would spread throughout the empire that he was alive and well. His sons would rediscover their filial sentiments, or at least be intimidated, and banish all traitorous thoughts from their minds. Under the circumstances, with not much room to manoeuvre, Prince Dara sought to raise a large army to supplement the imperial forces at his disposal and ordered that men be enlisted in the cities of Agra, Delhi and Lahore. He also sent word to a large section of the imperial army led by battle-hardened commanders, now stationed in the Deccan to subdue the sultanate of Bijapur, to immediately return to Agra. Word had come in that Aurangzeb had been trying to cajole and bribe the commanders to embrace his cause but most of the veterans obeyed the imperial summons and returned to the capital.

People who say Prince Dara was ignorant of military affairs and irresolute in pursuing them have not been witnesses to the activity that gripped his court in the following days. The libel that he was merely an impractical dreamer has been spread by Aurangzeb and his lapdog historians. It is wrong to assume that a man of action cannot be sensitive, that a good general must be a boor and never a poet. In times of peace, the Wali Ahad might have banished all thoughts of war from his mind and it may have appeared to onlookers that he was born only for pleasure and for the love of religion and philosophy. But once war was imminent, the warrior blood of his Mogul ancestors coursed mightily through his veins, transforming him from a genial scholar and *bon vivant* to an intrepid general.

The first decisive move on the part of the rebels was made by Shuja, the youngest of the princes, who proclaimed himself emperor at Rajmahal, the capital of Bengal, ordered coins to be struck in his name, and began to move westwards with his army. Prince Dara had always believed that as both warrior and consummate diplomat Shuja posed a graver threat to him than Aurangzeb. Aurangzeb he had despised for years as a hypocritical *namazi*. He now took Aurangzeb's caution and prudence in not marching immediately to Agra as a lack of decisiveness and dash.

His father did not share the Wali Ahad's apprehension about Shuja, nor his underestimation of Aurangzeb. 'Shuja may have been hardy and resolute once but his seventeen-year viceroyalty of Bengal has recast him in the softer mould of that province,' the emperor said. 'His sword has grown rusty in its scabbard for want of action in that land of peace, plenty and pestilence. He possesses no other quality now than an appetite for the enjoyment of life. Aurangzeb, if he ever decides to rebel, will be a more dangerous adversary. Remember that, my son.'

Yet, when news came of Shuja's act of rebellion—it was reported that he had led his commanders on their westward march with the cry of 'Ya takht, ya tabut! (The throne, or the coffin!)'—the emperor was reluctant to initiate action against him.

We saw the prince's frustration mount every time he returned from his daily audience with his father. 'The emperor refuses to recognize the threat. He has sent a *farman* yet again that Shuja should immediately withdraw,' he fumed.

'The emperor should understand by now that *farman*s are no longer enough to overawe any of those rebellious ingrates,' said Wazir Khan, voicing a sentiment that the Wali Ahad's filial loyalty prevented him from expressing.

It was a foregone conclusion that Shuja would ignore the imperial order. He announced that he knew his father was dead and the said *farman* was forged by Prince Dara in the name of the monarch. But if Shuja should find the emperor alive when he reached Agra, the prince would beg the emperor's forgiveness and submit to his authority.

Still, the monarch remained unmovable. 'You need patience, my son,' he counselled the anxious Prince Dara. 'This is your only failing, the lack of patience. You will see that Shuja will soon come to his senses and turn back.'

In early December there was further news: Shuja had crossed into Bihar with a large army that was coordinating its march with war boats sailing up the Ganges. The emperor reluctantly gave in to Prince Dara's entreaties, reinforced by Jahanara Begum's vigorous appeals, that they needed to act immediately. An army, 22,000 strong, under the command of Prince Dara's eldest son Sulaiman Shukoh, was asked to proceed against the rebels. Raja Jai Singh of Jaipur, an experienced and able commander, was appointed guardian and adviser to the young prince.

A brilliant and valorous youth of twenty-two, Prince Sulaiman was a loveable young man who was unfailingly courteous to high and low alike. I had met him but a few times at his father's palace, but he never failed to enquire after my health and even good-humouredly asked if he could be of any assistance.

'Perhaps a few flagons of my father's excellent liquor?' he would offer with a wink, alluding to my well-known weakness. 'When you return to *farangi* lands, Manucci, let no one there say that the Mughals do not know how to look after their guests.' Invariably, the wine, including at least two flagons of the highly regarded Persian Ab-i-Naad, would be delivered to my house the very next day.

On a crisp winter morning we gathered to witness the Wali Ahad bid farewell to the young prince. The sky was a clear azure blue. Drops of dew glistened on the freshly mowed grass of the lawn and on the poppies and rose petals in the flower beds. When father and son emerged from the prince's apartments, their faces showed contrasting emotions. Pride, worry and love were writ on the face of our prince, while Sulaiman's indisputable love for his father was veiled at this moment in impatience. He was in high spirits, eager to leave on an expedition that promised him glory. Fame beckoned, and he was keen to embrace it. Prince Dara held the reins as Sulaiman mounted his horse, and continued to deliver to the young man a stream of instructions till the very last moment before the young prince and his guards trotted out of the gate and disappeared down the road. A soft silence surged back once the plunging of hooves faded away, broken momentarily by Khwaja Younis who, exercising the privilege of a eunuch, began to weep noisily.

Moved by the moment and in the unease of what the ensuing days would deliver, I could not anticipate that Prince Dara's concern for his son's welfare was to have, instead, an unforeseen and most unfortunate consequence. In his anxiety, the prince had deputed his most faithful and able officers to serve under his beloved son. It was an act of fatherly love, the purest of impulses, but one which lacked foresight and was ill-advised for his own fortune. Thus are a man's noblest acts of love laid low by the indifference of fate.

In his preoccupation with Shuja's advance from the east and of his son's departure, the Wali Ahad did not ignore the danger from his two brothers in the west and the south. Everyone in the capital knew that Murad Baksh and Aurangzeb had formed a secret alliance, but were unaware of its full import. Prince Dara looked for ways to break the coalition. Initially, he succeeded in persuading the emperor to send a *farman* to Murad ordering him to take over the governorship of Berar, which was under Aurangzeb's control.

'If Murad obeys His Majesty's order, it will set him up in conflict with Aurangzeb,' the prince confided to his closest advisers. 'If he refuses, then his rebellion is out in the open, a circumstance the emperor is not always willing to recognize as fact.'

Murad ignored the order and continued his preparations to declare himself the emperor of Hindustan.

The tidings from the Deccan, where Aurangzeb was making his plans, were sketchy but ominous. He had secured all the ferries at the crossing of the Narmada, the river that forms a natural boundary between Hindustan and the Deccan, thus interdicting the courier routes. Yet sufficient news trickled through to fuel our unease. Aurangzeb, normally short and reserved with people, had apparently become all sweetness and honey in trying to woo the Deccan kings whom he had so recently fought and defeated, evidently in order to ensure his army's safety from an attack from the rear when he finally made his move in the direction of Agra.

In addition, he had apologized to the king of Bijapur for invading his kingdom and had even made placatory moves to gain the loyalty of Shivaji, a rebel chieftain who was proving to be a nuisance by carrying out swift guerilla attacks on the Mogul forces. Not only had Aurangzeb sent Shivaji presents and a gold tablet, but he had also promised the Hindu ruler one-fourth of the revenue of some of the Mogul provinces in the Deccan if the latter remained neutral in the approaching conflict.

Prince Dara listened to the reports in amusement. 'That must have been especially galling. Aurangzeb hates the Shias, whom he calls apostates, as much as he despises the Hindus,' he remarked. He called for a copy of a letter Aurangzeb had written to Jahanara Begum some fourteen years earlier and proceeded to read from it: '"Of all the wild beasts on land or water the wildest is an apostate, one who casts even the slightest doubt on the supremacy of Prophet Mohammed . . ." What a hypocrite, that *namazi!*'

'Do not underestimate him, O Prince,' Wazir Khan cautioned. 'Aurangzeb's moves show him to be a realist who can temporarily sacrifice matters of faith for political necessity. That makes him all the more dangerous.'

'A snake is dangerous but will slink away if met with determined force,' Prince Dara retorted.

As it happened, it was not Aurangzeb but Murad Baksh in Gujarat who followed Shuja in having himself crowned emperor, first in secret and then, two weeks later, in a public ceremony. Again the emperor did nothing more than send his usual *farman* ordering Murad to desist from rebellion.

Prince Dara was not unconcerned about Murad's proclamation, nor was he indifferent to Murad's further action of dispatching an army of three thousand horsemen, under the command of his loyal and wise eunuch Shahbaz, to pillage Surat and take control of the imperial treasury. What worried him more were the details of the secret pact between Aurangzeb and Murad that were made available to him by a highly placed spy in Murad's entourage who was successful in making copies of the letters exchanged between the two younger brothers and smuggling them to the prince.

'Be it known to the mighty Prince Murad Baksh that I have received word that Prince Dara has killed our father by poison and has taken possession of the government,' Aurangzeb's letter said. It went on to accuse Prince Dara of being an infidel and idolater, and declare Shuja to be a heretic, a follower of the sect of Ali. Thus there was no one except Murad who was worthy of ruling the Mogul empire. Aurangzeb himself, the poseur declared, had renounced the world a long time ago and had made a solemn vow to end his days at Mecca. It was only his 'zeal for the Quran' that had spurred him to devote his strength to ensuring that the empire was left in Murad's capable hands. All he asked was that after Murad was seated on the throne, he should look after Aurangzeb's family. 'I send you one hundred thousand rupees, in order to establish between us a firm and perpetual union and friendship, being brothers as we are, of one father and of one faith, and both defenders of the Quran.'

Murad had replied to the letter confirming his allegiance to Aurangzeb and to his cause of safeguarding the religion of the Quran, and accepting his brother's proposal.

After he had read out the exchange in court for all to hear, Wazir Khan fastened on the closing lines of Murad's letter: 'I am making ready for the joining of our two armies, to carry out what Allah the Most High shall inspire. Awaiting further news, and believing that there can be no doubt of what you have promised me, your faithful brother, Murad Baksh.' Handing over the scrolls to an attendant, he commented thoughtfully, 'He is still not quite certain of Aurangzeb's intentions. We need to exploit his doubt. We can arrange for another, similar letter from Aurangzeb but addressed to Shuja to fall into Murad's hands. To sow discord between allies is equal to neutralizing an army of fifty thousand soldiers.'

Before the prince could reply, Khalilullah Khan, commander of the imperial cavalry and Prince Dara's most trusted adviser on military affairs, rejected the suggestion. 'Dissimulation is a weapon of the weak. We are strong and assured of victory in battle. We must act now, and act decisively,' he said, vigorously massaging his right earlobe, as was his habit.

It was left to the prince to convince the emperor to initiate appropriate action. At first, the monarch insisted that the letters were forgeries. Roshanara Begum, the emperor's devious and illiterate younger daughter, much given to lasciviousness, forcefully supported the emperor's view. She was firmly in Aurangzeb's camp. We waited impatiently for the prince to convince the emperor otherwise and allow him to take whatever steps he thought necessary to checkmate the rebels.

It was almost the end of December when two armies, one under Qasim Khan and the other under Raja Jaswant Singh of Jodhpur, were sent to the south. Their mission was to block Aurangzeb from crossing the Narmada and prevent the armies of Murad and Aurangzeb from coming together. Whereas the courage and loyalty of the Rajput chief was beyond doubt, Qasim Khan was not well inclined towards our prince and accepted the imperial command most reluctantly.

In the days when we had first heard rumours of Aurangzeb's alliance with Murad, I was, one evening, summoned to Khalilullah Khan's mansion. It seemed that the noble's fourth wife, a girl of sixteen he had recently married, had been behaving strangely. She was completely listless, refusing to wash her body or comb her hair, and her eyes appeared unfocussed at all times. This, in combination with her lately developed habit of spending entire days leaning against a wall and swaying her head from side to side had convinced the hakims that she was possessed. A renowned Muslim exorcist, Pir Elahi, had attempted to free her of it but her condition had shown no improvement. The summons for me would have come earlier but for the fact that Muslim exorcists did not demand that the strict purdah of the harem be violated, whereas I always insisted on coming face to face with the possessed woman. In any event, I was successful in getting the satanic spirit to leave the poor girl's body after a single session lasting no more than an hour, and this even without a light beating with the cane, the final part of my exorcism ritual.

Before I left the harem, I was discreetly informed that Khalilullah Khan's first wife wished to speak to me privately and was escorted to the inner apartments by a eunuch, who was subsequently dismissed. The lady, I recalled, was rumoured to be one of the emperor's paramours, the famed 'Shah Jahan's lunch'.

I heard a strong but mellifluous voice from behind the curtain. 'Doctors are used to keeping secrets. What I want to tell you, *farangi* hakim, is only meant for the Wali Ahad's ears. Tell him to place no reliance on my husband nor trust his soft speeches. I know him well. At home, where he takes off his mask of good cheer and ingratiating manner, I am privy to the malice submerged in his cold smile and the malevolence he hides behind his hooded eyes. Given the occasion, he is bound to engineer some treachery. Remember to convey my words to the Wali Ahad.'

I was to leave for Delhi immediately after and did not get a chance to meet the prince. Instead, I passed on the message to Wazir Khan, who had looked upon me favourably ever since I had cured his wife. I have no doubt he conveyed the message further, if only because of his rivalry with Khalilullah and for the prince's ear and favour. I only know that the Wali Ahad did not take the warning seriously. Perhaps he attributed it to Khalilullah's wife's jealousy of her husband's new wife and dismissed it as the rants of a slighted woman.

'Aurangzeb may have dissembled often, but he was not a hypocrite'

FRANCOIS BERNIER

WE BEGAN OUR JOURNEY to Aurangabad, the new capital of the Mogul dominions in the Deccan, in the middle of February 1658 when the heat and dust were no longer intolerable. I was proud that the Agha had entrusted me with an important mission and excited that I would finally come face to face with the prince whose shadow loomed so large on the future shape of the empire. I was equally happy that I would no longer have to consume the badly baked bazaar bread of Delhi, crackling with sand and dust, or drink the capital's river water, whose impurities exceed my power of description since it is equally accessible to all men and animals and a receptacle of all manner of filth.

When we reached Gwalior, intending to halt there for a few days, we heard from the governor of the province that Aurangzeb had set out towards Agra with a large army. The Agha had indicated to me that the governor of Gwalior sympathized with Aurangzeb's cause but was as yet unaware of the Agha's own leanings. All he knew about us was that we served the powerful foreign minister of the imperial court and were on our way to the Deccan to confer with Mir Jumla, the chief commander of the section of the imperial army that had been sent to assist Aurangzeb in his conquest of the kingdom of Bijapur.

'Prince Aurangzeb has not proclaimed himself emperor. Not like the princes Murad and Shuja,' the governor said, trying to keep the excitement out of his voice. 'He is not a rebel but a dutiful son who is marching to Agra to rescue an ailing father from the clutches of the infidel Dara Shukoh.'

The governor's sharp eyes, narrowed into slits by the swelling folds of fleshy cheeks pressing against them, keenly searched our faces for any sign that might betray our loyalties. Finding none, he continued in a measured voice, attempting to maintain a stance of careful neutrality: 'I am told he has an army of thirty thousand veterans, reinforced by a few contingents of Maratha irregulars. I have heard that before he took to the field Aurangzeb ordered everyone to kneel on the ground, as he did himself, and ask God to grant them victory. He then raised his hands to heaven and said, "*Aya sar diham ya sitanam* (I will lose my own head or take my adversary's)".'

Keeping my face impassive, I inwardly applauded Aurangzeb's instinctive understanding and manipulation of symbols, so necessary for anyone who aspires to be a leader of men. His were the very words spoken by Alexander the Great when he marched against King Darius; Aurangzeb had absorbed Danishmand Khan's history lessons well.

'I also hear that the prince has imprisoned Mir Jumla and has taken command over his troops. Will you still be going to Aurangabad or should I make arrangements for your return to Agra?' the governor asked innocently.

'This is momentous news, indeed,' Imran Khan, who we had agreed would be our spokesman, said. 'We will need to discuss it further. Perhaps we shall presume on your hospitality for a few more days till the situation becomes clearer.'

'Bernier,' Imran Khan told me that evening, 'we shall stay in Gwalior and await further news of Aurangzeb's march. I have sent a courier to his camp to enquire where he would like to meet us.'

I confess I was not displeased at the prospect of resting for a few days, especially in the pleasurable company of Habshi, who I had insisted should accompany me on our journey to the Deccan but had not seen much of because of the exigencies of travel. Travelling in India is strenuous under the best of circumstances and the more difficult part of our route—the mountainous region of central Hindustan with its narrow roads hugging the sides of hills where even a sturdy young horse can slip and take its rider with it to the bottom of a ravine, and the streams littered with boulders and rocks where a wagon can easily overturn—was still before us.

Ill-built in the manner of most Indian towns, Gwalior is not particularly attractive, its only agreeable feature being its location on the side of a mountain and the high walls with towers that surrounds it. The fortress of Gwalior had a royal prison where Emperor Shah Jahan sent princes and nobles who had run foul of him for safe custody and eventual execution, a practice now continued by his successor. Within the fortress, on the northwest slope of the mountain, the emperor had built a pleasure palace from where the entire town was visible. The palace had an attached guest house where important dignitaries of the empire were put up and this was to be our residence for a week.

Unlike me, Imran Khan was impatient to complete our mission and return to Delhi where he could involve himself, however vicariously, in the political developments that were taking place in the capital city in our absence. As a foreigner and a person of a philosophical bent of mind, my interest in the events that the Omrah found so absorbing was more as an observer than a participant, although, I must concede, I was not always immune to the agitation that swirled all around me. I was content to spend my days taking up the translation of Descartes's *Discourse on the Method of Properly Conducting One's Reason*, which I had left untouched for more than six weeks while Habshi provided a welcome diversion from my intellectual labours. Three times a week we dined with the governor and avidly lapped up the news of the progress of the various rebellions.

When Aurangzeb finally made his move, it had been almost three
months since Shuja and Murad had each declared himself emperor.
Murad had been pressing him for weeks: 'We are losing time and
letting our business suffer by waiting for certain news of the emperor.
Our enemy is getting stronger. Let us start together for Agra. It only
remains for you to give the order,' he had apparently written to his
brother in one of innumerable missives. But Aurangzeb had waited
patiently till he felt he had secured the rear of his army and convinced
Mir Jumla to secretly switch sides and surrender his treasure, cavalry
and especially his artillery, which boasted some of the best Dutch and
French gunners, thus adding significant strength to Aurangzeb's arms.
I have seen those huge guns, some forty-eight pounders, others thirty-
six pounders, each gun drawn by twenty-four pairs of oxen. Strong
and powerful elephants followed the artillery and were employed in
pushing the guns with their trunks whenever the oxen had difficulty in
drawing the gun carriage. Mir Jumla being imprisoned by Aurangzeb
for his refusal to betray the imperial cause was thus a mere fiction
created to safeguard the lives of the officer's wife and three children
who were being held hostage at the imperial court in Agra by Dara.

It was clear that Aurangzeb deliberated for long before reaching
a decision, but once he was set on a course of action he moved with
dispatch. Within thirteen days, he reached Burhanpur, the old capital
of Mogul Deccan, commanding the ferry points on the river Narmada,
where he set up camp outside the city and waited for Murad's army
to join his forces for their joint advance on Agra. The courier we had
dispatched returned with the message that Aurangzeb was planning
to stay for a month in Burhanpur, a town which for me carried fond
memories of the merchant lad Afzal, who had sought to introduce me
to catamite pleasures that I had witlessly spurned at the time. Imran
Khan and I decided it was now time for us to seek the audience of
the prince.

The countryside between Gwalior and Burhanpur is generally
flat, with fertile fields of wheat and rice, and many small towns and
although we had to ford many small streams that were now dry, we

made good progress, covering around forty miles a day, thanks also to the governor who had arranged for fresh horses and provisions to be provided to our party at suitable intervals. We passed occasional trading caravans on our way but I got the distinct impression that these were few and far between. As compared to my journey in the opposite direction during the early part of the year, when I was on my way to join Danishmand Khan's court, the serais where we halted had conspicuously fewer guests; when armies march, all other movement along the route they take comes to a halt as people seek the safety of their homes and animals scurry to take shelter in the woods.

As it transpired, we did not get to Burhanpur. On receiving a message from Murad that the latter would join him further north, near the woods of Mandu, Aurangzeb's army had set out in late March to cross the Narmada while we were still on our way. We had no option but to halt halfway on the Great Deccan Road, in Ujjain, a town sacred to the idolaters on the bank of the river Sipra, and then meet Aurangzeb at his camp some fifty miles southwest of Ujjain, where his army had pitched tents as it waited for Murad's. It was thus on the sixteenth day of April, 1658, that Imran Khan and I reached Aurangzeb's camp and, late in the morning of the following day, presented ourselves outside the prince's tent after he had returned from an inspection of his elite cavalry regiment which, along with the artillery, was under his direct command.

Physically, Aurangzeb was lean and very tall, of a fairer complexion than is otherwise prevalent among his countrymen. His beard, too, was a dark brown rather than black. Instead of the rich robes favoured by the Omrah, he wore a battlefield *jubba*, a beige coat made of thick, quilted silk that was capable of withstanding the blow of a sword or the impact of a ball from a musket. He welcomed us with signal courtesy though his countenance remained characteristically grave, its solemnity enhanced by impassive eyes that could occasionally turn speculative. Whenever he smiled, which was rare, one could see the effort in the muscles around his mouth to hold the smile in its place. His voice was soft, his manner mild, and my first impression of him—

which I have had no reason to revise—was immediately favourable. Before he and Imran Khan disappeared into the tent to discuss matters of strategy, he called on one of his personal officers.

'Take the *farangi* doctor around the encampment,' he commanded. 'I am very interested in his observations on my army and how it compares to that of a European king.'

I did not need to traverse the entire encampment to note that Aurangzeb's camp bore little resemblance to similar camps in Europe. More than a military camp, it was like a large town, its habitations segregated accorded to rank, its inhabitants a motley mix of different communities—Moguls, Afghans, Marathas and contingents from Golconda—each with its own commander and its own war cry, its own preferred weapons and way of fighting. The Golconda soldiers, for instance, do not wear sabres like the Persians but a broad sword like the Swiss, with which they cut and thrust; a cavalryman carries a bow and arrows, a buckler and a battle axe, and is protected by a metal head-piece and a jacket of mail that hangs down from the head-piece over the shoulders. Lacking a common uniform, each contingent of the Mogul army dresses in the manner of its community and each individual within it according to his choosing, further reinforcing the impression of an Indian town, unlike its European counterpart, which would certainly look like a battlement.

The tents of the high-ranking *mansabdar*s were pitched around Aurangzeb's own tent, which was at the centre of the encampment. Each tent flew a flag of a different colour and shape, making for a colourful spectacle. The further one moved away from the centre, the lower was the station of the soldier and the poorer the accommodation, until one reached the ordinary soldier who slept in the open under a tree or under a sheet of cloth tied to four wooden poles as protection against the night dew, his single weapon and meagre possessions kept on the ground next to him. Many of these soldiers—and here I include wrestlers, water-carriers, palanquin bearers and other menials (though not the shopkeepers who tag along with an army) who are all classed as infantry by the Moguls—had their wives and children with them in the camp. Indeed, with the mobilization of troops affecting all parts of the country, I had seen scores of soldiers on their way to join the armies that were being raised, some carrying unweaned infants in their arms, baskets of cooking pots and pans on their heads, while their wives marched behind them with spears or matchlocks upon their backs.

The camp was busier than a town on a market day. Since it was nearing lunchtime, cooking fires were ablaze at various places in the camp; the mingled smell of different cuisines would have easily turned a European stomach more fastidious than mine. Elephants were being washed by their mahouts, robust Turkish horses were being massaged by their grooms, soldiers were engaged in polishing their weapons or applying coats of black varnish to their leather shields, which had scores of inch-long nails protruding from them. I was not surprised to see that very few were involved in taking care of their muskets, an activity that is considered *de rigueur* in a European army. Father Roth had told me that Mogul musketeers, who have a low status in the army, are terribly afraid of burning their beards, or of their guns bursting in the course of being fired, and regard their weapons with some dread. In battle, they are careful to keep the muskets at a safe distance from them, firing them not from the shoulder but from a squatting position while resting them on wooden forks.

In the days that followed, while I wandered around the camp observing its goings-on, or worked on my translation in my tent, Imran Khan spent his time ingratiating himself with Aurangzeb's officers in case their prince indeed ascended the throne. It is from him that I later learnt that Aurangzeb was a worried man during his stay at Mandu, though the creases of worry never furrowed his brow in public. Or perhaps his air of equanimity was real, a consequence of his firm belief that he was an instrument of Divine will; that Allah was all and man was nothing; that human victories and defeats occurred in accordance with Allah's will, and all He required of man was the acceptance of happenings that were preordained.

The prince indeed had cause for worry. After weeks of pressing Aurangzeb to commit troops to the field, Murad had suddenly become tardy in his own advance. Reports had reached Aurangzeb that Shahbaz, Murad's trusted adviser, was counselling his master against their joint venture. Eunuchs are naturally suspicious and do not hold human nature in high esteem; yet they are intensely devoted to their masters, even when the master is as boorish and devoid of good sense as Murad. One of Aurangzeb's agents brought news of Shahbaz telling Murad in open court, 'Do not trust your brother's sweet words. Mistrust is the mother of safety. An excess of respect and too smooth a tongue hides a treacherous heart. Remain in Gujarat and become the master of its flourishing towns like Surat, which will greatly add to your treasure. Let us wait, and time will show us what we should do.'

Aurangzeb had reacted by sending Murad letters which reaffirmed his determination to make his brother the emperor of Hindustan. I have seen one of the letters which came into Imran Khan's possession for an hour before it was dispatched. I can vouch for Aurangzeb's epistolary subtlety and knowledge of human character, especially its weaknesses. In this letter, he had used the most effusive vocabulary to flatter Murad, holding out again the promise of a glorious future and thereby minimizing the risk of anything going wrong with their plans to supplant Dara. In profound words Aurangzeb had reiterated that for himself he wished nothing more than seeking refuge in Mecca and living there like the fakir he was in the deepest recesses of his heart: 'I have not the slightest wish to take any part in the governing of this deceitful and unstable world . . . My desire is that I should retire to a secret corner and spend my days and nights in the worship of the Almighty whose blessings constitute the only true happiness. But then I thought that first I should place my dear brother firmly on the throne, and after witnessing his auspicious and successful coronation, and gathering happiness and pleasure from it, return to fulfil my heart's desire.' He went on to humbly enquire if, when he did retire from material life, he could entrust the care of his two sons to Murad. As their guardian, Murad was to show them no special favour but deal with them like any other man in his service. I found the sentiments expressed in the letter both heartfelt and admirable, further increasing my appreciation for the prince's character.

Meanwhile, Aurangzeb's agents at Murad's court had been persistent in assuring Murad of his brother's sincere intentions of seeing him on the throne of the Indies. Murad's ambition, allied with Aurangzeb's subtle flattery, finally triumphed over Shahbaz's counsel of prudence. The two armies came together near the woods of Mandu where Aurangzeb had impatiently awaited his brother.

Was Prince Aurangzeb's wooing of his brother simple hypocrisy, especially in the light of later events, as many of his critics maintain? I pride myself on my objectivity in judging people independent of my likes and dislikes, a quality ingrained in me by M. Gassendi, and one that induced the Agha to entrust me with the mission to Aurangzeb's camp. After spending more than six weeks with the prince, and observing him at close quarters and in moments of crisis, I can say that Aurangzeb may have dissembled often, but he was not a hypocrite; a hypocrite disavows his primary intention, which I have not witnessed in Aurangzeb's behaviour. Aurangzeb's primary goal was to safeguard Islamic rule in India, which Dara Shukoh's ascension to the throne would have weakened if not destroyed. His desire to be emperor and his hatred of Dara, both of which were intense and certainly fuelled his acts, were nevertheless secondary to this end. If he lied to Murad as he did to others, or committed even baser deeds in pursuance of his goal, then they were but means to an end to which he remained steadfastly committed all his life: the defence and spread of the Mohammedan faith. It is another matter that he honoured a false prophet, denied the religion of our Saviour and like all Mohammedans believed Islam to be the only true religion while despising other faiths as inferior.

I remember the evening before the armies were to move, when the prince called his commanders to his tent and spoke about his reasons for going to war. He had invited Imran Khan and I to be present.

'A prince has only two bounden duties: to dispense equal justice to everyone and to work ceaselessly for the furtherance of Allah's glory and the propagation of His faith. The great Timurlang, my ancestor and the illustrious founder of the empire, was a rare and magnificent exemplar of both these qualities. Cries of the oppressed called him to take up arms against Bayazid, the emperor of the Turks. If that disgusting infidel Dara ascends the throne, the religion of Mohammed will be persecuted and the country will resound with the cries of tyrannized Mohammedans. Instead of noble mosques, hideous temples crowded with idols of gargoyles will be erected all over the land. Instead of congregations of pious men, modest and God-fearing, who ceaselessly proclaim the greatness and virtues of Allah, what you will have are taverns and houses of ill-fame spreading their poison in devout Mohammedan households. This is what we are fighting against, not for the self-seeking glory of a prince.'

If I, a foreigner and a Christian at that, found myself stirred by the speech, more by its content than its quiet delivery, then one can imagine how moved the Mohammedan commanders must have been by the sentiments that animated the speaker. I also witnessed how the officers' emotional reactions percolated down to the men they commanded, to the ordinary soldier who did not love him—Prince Aurangzeb was too remote to evoke any such sentiment—but deeply respected him as a *ghazi*, a warrior who is also, or almost, a saint.

While in the company of his troops I heard the many stories that circulated about his piety and humility, often recounted in a tone of awe. Once, while in Aurangabad, when the prince was on his way to the mosque, one of the officials noticed that the carpet on which he would have to tread had a hole in it and hurried to cover the hole with a piece of cloth. Noticing his action, Aurangzeb severely reproved the man, saying all that fussing over him was fine at court but had no place in Allah's house where a prince was no higher than a common man. Then there was the time when he got up at night to pray—he sat for prayer at least five times a day—and ordered a eunuch to bring him water to wash his hands and feet, a ritual prescribed for

Mohammedans when they offer *namaz*. In his hurry, the eunuch, who was scarcely awake, stumbled and knocked the prince down. Overcome with fear of punishment, he collapsed before Aurangzeb in a blubbering heap. The prince is said to have addressed him in the mildest of tones: 'Why do you dread a man who is like yourself, a created being? Such fear should be reserved for Allah, so be aware only of offending Him.'

If I were to be completely honest, however, I would say that Aurangzeb was pious in his personal life but also used piety for his other passion: power. In this, he was not unlike one of our famous French poets (whom I shall not name out of a sense of propriety), who is a poet only when composing his verses, while at other times he uses the same poetry in his favourite enterprise: the seduction of women admirers.

What stood out for me was Aurangzeb's simplicity, which contrasted greatly with the lavish display favoured by the other princes and the Omrah. On an invitation to dinner in his tent, I was immediately astonished by the bareness of its furnishings. There were no silk carpets, no velvet and silk drapings, no gold or silver bedsteads, just a simple white cotton sheet spread on the floor, and his bed was a mat he had woven out of straw with his own hands. The only valuable piece of furniture was a low carved table made from walnut wood, on which rested a gilded copy of the Quran. The dinner served before us was lavish, with special dishes of deer and pheasant, which abound in the forests of Mandu, but the prince, while urging us on in the manner of a good host to partake of larger portions of each dish, ate a simple fare of rice, lentils, a preparation of bitter gourd and a salad of fresh pink radishes. He reminded me at that moment of M. Gassendi who, too, would host lavish dinners for his guests and serve the most delectable meals—smoked ham with anise, duck in a savoury orange sauce, capons stuffed with oysters, delicious pastries—but eat very little of these delicacies himself. 'I prefer the simpler fare of older times,' he would say when the guests had left, 'everything boiled in the same pot. An obsession with food is a sign of a man who secretly regards his mind as an enemy.' I enjoyed my meal thoroughly that day at the prince's tent, more so since, to my relief, I did not have to chew paan (betel leaf, which tastes like soap and colours the mouth red) at the end of the repast, an Indian habit to which I have never become reconciled in spite of spending so many years in the Mogul dominions. The prince himself disliked paan and instead chewed a gum called *kharadali* which, thankfully, he did not offer to us.

Many people in Europe have asked me my impressions of Aurangzeb's person. He has been spoken of as a cold and distant man, but I believe he was simply different from his countrymen who are excitable and much given to histrionics. Aurangzeb was naturally reserved and his matter-of-fact, dry manner of expression might have made him appear remote to people with a weakness for hyperbole. I found the prince to be unlike other Indians I became acquainted with, who were either incurable romantics or embittered cynics. He was of a breed rarely found in the Indies: a realist.

'He is as acidic as his favorite fruit, the corinda,' I had heard Father Buze say of the prince. But the good father, for all his qualities of head and heart, was a biased observer who had cultivated a taste for the effusive sweetness of Dara's nature that I personally found cloying.

Few people were aware that there was another side to the younger prince's nature. During my weeks at his camp, the commander of his cavalry, a grizzled veteran who had been with the prince since his first campaign at the age of seventeen, told me of the prince's infatuation with a dancing girl named Hirabai when he was thirty-five years old and already the father of six children. During the two years that this liaison lasted, the bouts of melancholy that had earlier often possessed the prince miraculously disappeared. Hirabai was as accomplished a musician and dancer as she was beautiful and Aurangzeb could not have enough either of the singer or her songs.

'I have not seen him as lighthearted as he was during those two years,' the officer said. 'He smiled more often, even laughed at witticisms that began to be made at his court, though hesitantly at first. He was ready to do anything for Hirabai. Once, when she told him that if he really loved her he would flout the Islamic prohibition against drinking wine, he immediately ordered a flagon of Shiraz wine and two golden goblets to be brought to them. Hirabai stopped him as he was about to raise the glass to his lips. 'You have convinced me, my lord,' she said. 'I require no further proof of your love and may Allah forgive me for even trying to test your religious convictions.'

Hirabai, renamed Zainabadi by Aurangzeb, died suddenly, a month after the prince's thirty-seventh birthday, and with her demise layers of ice again began to form on the surface of his soul. The bouts of melancholy became deeper and lasted longer. After he received the news of her death, he is reported to have ridden out to hunt in a state of high agitation, saying that all the lamentations in his house would not give him the same relief as the solitude of a hunt. A week after her funeral, he gathered his senior officers for a meeting and said that Allah had been merciful to him by putting an end to the dancing girl's life since his preoccupation with her had diverted him from the real purpose of his life. He never listened to music again.

I found it admirable that Aurangzeb had absorbed a fundamental lesson of kingship even before he became emperor: that the price the Almighty demands for raising a man to the pinnacles of glory and power is a steeling of the heart. Not for him the open-faced delight, taken as a God-given right by even the most abject of his subjects, to give and receive love that will leave him vulnerable. A king may love his horse, his dog, his country, but never other human beings except, sometimes, his spouse or a child. He may be as rich as Croesus but must be the greatest miser in expending trust lest it be betrayed. Compelled to forego intimacy with those who surround him, he is reduced to offering it to the rest of the world. The king belongs to his subjects because he may never belong to anything or anyone else.

The arrival of Murad with his army was one of the few occasions that brought a smile to Aurangzeb's face, a smile that otherwise never reached his eyes. Aurangzeb, together with his son Sultan Muhammad, his chief nobles and officers of the personal guard, rode out a mile from the camp to greet Murad. He received his brother with great respect, standing before him as a subordinate would, his shoulders bowed and his hands crossed in front of him. In the hearing of their officer corps, he addressed his brother as 'my king' or 'my sovereign' and then renewed the pledge he had made earlier, swearing allegiance to Murad against the infidel Dara. A roar of approval rose among the nobles and officers from both sides when the brothers embraced.

Two days later, the joint armies marched fourteen miles towards the river near Ujjain, where the imperial forces were waiting to thwart their crossing to the opposite bank. The march had acquired an urgency because of disquieting news from Bengal—the 'hell, well stocked with rice' as Aurangzeb called it—which reached the prince that very evening, after his meeting with Murad.

The battle near the village of Dharmat on the twenty-eighth day of April, was short and sharp, lasting no more than five hours. It ended in total defeat for the imperial forces when Qasim Khan, who had been bribed by Aurangzeb beforehand, suddenly quit the battlefield, leaving Raja Jaswant Singh and his nine thousand Rajputs exposed to rebel forces almost three times their number. The battle was enormously instructive for anyone interested in comparing the fighting skills and battle strategies of Indians with those of Europeans. As a physician, albeit one trained in the treatment of battle injuries, I am not an expert in military affairs and strategies but can provide a layman's impressions, which those with far greater expertise than mine may still find of some value.

The first thing that strikes an observer is the lack of order in an Indian army. The chaos is so pronounced, in fact, that even when the two armies are fiercely engaged in fighting each other, the number of those killed on the battlefield rarely exceeds a few hundred since, before long, one or the other side invariably resorts to panicky flight. As a fighting force the infantry is nearly worthless, an ill-equipped and ill-disciplined rabble that is more a liability than an asset in war.

I noticed in this particular battle that the only soldiers who fought were those well forward while most of those who were closer to the rear did nothing but shout '*Ba-kush! Ba-kush!*' and '*Mar! Mar!* (Kill, kill!)', while waving their unsheathed swords in the air. In general, if the men in the front advance, those behind follow in their steps, and if the former retire the others flee. Once they begin their flight it is impossible to stop them, with the result that the huge army can melt away in a matter of minutes. The fear of cavalry is so great among Indian soldiers that forty thousand infantry will not stand up against two thousand horsemen. The European practice of a line of men with spears and pikes standing ahead of the infantry to blunt a cavalry charge is almost unthinkable in India. Here, the foot soldiers begin to run nearly as fast as the horses gallop as soon as horsemen come into sight, even if the riders are not carrying any firearms.

The exception to such behaviour on the battlefield are the Pathans, an Afghan tribe from the northwest region of the empire, and the Rajputs, a caste of idolater warriors whom I have mentioned earlier. The Rajputs, who bore the brunt of casualties at Dharmat, are formidable fighters who only require to be directed by a competent leader, and on his part the leader need never entertain the apprehension that the men under his command will flee since Rajputs look upon a retreat from battle as the greatest disgrace that can befall them. Defeated Moguls show their submission by presenting themselves with two swords hanging around their necks and a shroud in their hands; Afghans surrender with grass between their teeth, implying bovine submission to the victor; Turks surrender with their turbans in the hands—but since Rajputs never surrender they have no ritual acknowledgement of defeat. On the day of battle, they ingest a large quantity of opium in order to dull their senses to all danger and provide them with the courage to rush unhesitatingly into fierce combat. To see them before they enter the battlefield with their saffron-coloured bandanas tied around the heads, a symbol of their funeral shroud, fumes of opium making their eyes shine with unnatural light, embracing and bidding adieu to one another as if certain of death, is remarkable indeed. To kill or be killed is the only tenet that guides their conduct in battle and that is, ironically, what sets them back. To retreat tactically in order to regroup is as much a part of a battle as fierce and courageous fighting, and since a retreat is out of question for the Rajputs, they tend to lack general strategic sense as well. Inspecting the battlefield at Dharmat littered with corpses of Rajput warriors, Aurangzeb had expressed disdain for what he called their 'crass stupidity'. 'As their fundamental rule is to be either victorious or die, it is little wonder that most of the time they die rather than win. Sometimes, to part with your head rather than retreat from your position is not a sign of courage but simply of foolishness,' he remarked.

Yet, the courage possessed by Rajputs, however imprudent it may be, makes them extremely valuable as soldiers in a country where soldiering is a part-time activity for most troopers. Every Mogul emperor ensures that his rajas are treated with care and honour and has been known to shower them with favours. He needs the chieftains and their soldiers on his side to keep in check other rajas who are not in his pay and to induce the submission of those who refuse to pay tribute or take up arms against the empire. For instance, the alliance with the Rajputs had proved invaluable for the Moguls against the kings of Bijapur and Golconda in the Deccan, or when they were engaged in hostilities against the Persians. In these engagements, the monarch could not trust most of his Omrah, who are of Persian origin and share the Shia faith of the Deccan kings. A few might even consider it a mortal sin to take up arms against the Persian sovereign, whom, as a descendant of the Prophet's grandson, Ali, they acknowledge as their Imam.

The Rajput women are just as valorous as their men, seeing their husbands and sons off to battle, or even certain death, with a fervour that will be incomprehensible to Europeans. I have heard of instances from the past, when the besieged defenders of a fort, finding their situation hopeless, sallied out to meet their end at the hands of the Mogul army while back in the fort the women collectively immolated themselves in the name of Rajput honour by throwing themselves into a huge pyre constructed expressly for the purpose. The extremes to which the human mind can traverse under the influence of ancient customs, prejudice, public opinion and the principle of honour is truly astounding.

I was thus hardly surprised to hear about the misfortune that befell Raja Jaswant Singh of Jodhpur after the defeat of the imperial forces. The courageous Rajput had had to quit the battlefield at Dharmat, in spite of putting up a valiant fight, after he was deserted by the treacherous Qasim Khan and had lost close to eight thousand of his men. Qasim Khan had, in fact, gone so far as to secretly bury his artillery ammunition for later use by Aurangzeb's forces. The raja started for his own country, seventy leagues from the scene of his defeat, with the remaining contingent of less than five hundred horsemen. By the time he reached Jodhpur, his companions had shrunk to fifteen. Ashamed to show their faces to their countrymen in defeat, the rest had melted away. His actions had arisen from necessity, not dishonour, yet when the exhausted and dejected king approached the gates of his capital city, his wife, the daughter of one of the Ranas of Udaipur, who are universally regarded as the epitome of Rajput honour and, in contrast to the rajas of Jaipur and Jodhpur, have never sought service with the Moguls, ordered that the gates of Jodhpur be closed to her husband.

'The man reeks of infamy,' she is said to have declared. 'I disown him as my husband. No son-in-law of the Rana can possess a soul so abject that he quits the battlefield rather than dying on it. Now I shall have neither the renown of a hero's wife nor an honoured widow's death by burning.' Her rage and passion were so extreme that she conceived the fancy that Jaswant Singh had actually perished in battle and that the truth was being concealed from her so as to prevent her from burning herself to death as a *sati*. 'Prepare the funeral pyre and let the fire consume my body,' she ordered. 'My husband is certainly dead; it cannot be otherwise.' This went on for eight to nine days till the arrival of her mother, who calmed her with assurances that once her husband had recovered from his exhaustion, he would raise another army to fight Aurangzeb and regain his honour. She reluctantly reconciled herself to this course of action but constantly insulted her husband and forbade him to ever share her bed again. It is said that once when a maidservant brought a melon to the raja along with a knife to cut it, the queen pounced on the poor woman, beating her and shouting, 'How dare you bring a knife! Don't you know the courage of this runaway? He swoons when he sees iron of any kind.'

Whatever the conduct of the soldiers on the battlefield, the victory at Dharmat, which Aurangzeb immediately renamed Fatehbad, 'habitation of victory', emboldened the armies of the two princes and removed any doubts the officers and soldiers had entertained about tackling the imperial army. Walking around Aurangzeb's camp in the evening, I heard men boast that there was no army in the world that could oppose them and that after they had become masters of the empire they would press ahead to conquer Persia and Turkey. To me this seemed to be misplaced overconfidence. I also heard some talk about differences arising between the brothers on the next course of action. Murad wanted to press ahead immediately, without giving his troops time to rest so as to take advantage of the disarray in the imperial ranks and engage Dara before the latter's son Sulaiman could join him with his army of battle-hardened veterans. Aurangzeb was more circumspect. He wanted to send his spies to Agra to ascertain the exact state of affairs, with letters to his friends at the court promising great rewards to defectors from Dara's cause. Aurangzeb's views finally prevailed and the armies rested on the banks of the river before resuming their advance, which was to be regulated according to the information being received from Agra. Meanwhile, the ammunition left behind by Qasim Khan was dug up and distributed between the two armies, significantly boosting their capabilities.

Here I should add that Qasim Khan never received the riches promised to him for his betrayal of Dara. Aurangzeb was a principled man who was willing to dissemble and deceive in service of his political and military aims but held fast to his moral conviction that a traitor should never be rewarded but should, on the contrary, be punished with death after he is no longer useful. It was the prince's maxim to put traitors to death by slow poisoning so he would not have to suffer the same perfidy. 'Anyone who has betrayed his master once is fully capable of betraying a new one,' he said. He held, however, that the traitor's children and grandchildren were to be treated with great munificence: 'Nothing douses the flames of revenge as well as a shower of silver.' In his sense of morality, of what is right and what is wrong, Aurangzeb is indeed an exception among Mogul princes and not the scheming hypocrite naïvely portrayed by Dara's sympathizers.

We were still encamped at Dharmat when Imran Khan and I went to Aurangzeb's tent to take the prince's permission to leave for Agra and return to our Agha, Danishmand Khan. He had just finished his noon prayers and his reading of the Quran and was about to leave for an inspection of his troops.

Aurangzeb's concern for his troopers, his attention to detail, is a rarity. I have not seen anything similar even among European princes. To us he was as polite as always, his voice low, his hollow-cheeked face sombre in spite of the recent triumph. 'Tell your Agha that my victory is foreordained. When the battle with Dara's forces is finally over within a few days, more than forty thousand Mughals will cross over to my side. Tell him also that mine is not a war for the throne but obedience to the command of Allah who whispered in my ear, as He often does at crucial moments, that I must fight the forces of *kufr* and unrighteousness unleashed by my brother Dara Shukoh. My ears are ever attuned to hearing His voice. Material rewards and riches are mere shadows, empty husks that leave me cold. Obedience to Allah's will is the only crown I seek. Islam is the breath of my life. Allah has chosen me to be the custodian of the faithful in Hindustan. I shall not let Islam perish or be diluted by apostasy. This is my pledge, first to my Creator and then to all of you.' I walked away from the short audience impressed by the sincerity in his voice and the strength of conviction that gripped his heart.

I was as glad to be back in Delhi, now its normal hot and dusty self, as I had been glad to leave it three months earlier when the city was at its most pleasant. The Agha listened to my enthusiastic endorsement of Prince Aurangzeb's character and prospects, which I gave in substantially the same words that I have employed in my writings, with his usual grave courtesy. 'You have done well, Bernier, but then I never expected anything less,' he commented as I finished. But the pensive look that overshadowed his face as I took my leave, left me perplexed.

Two days later, Khwaja Chisti provided a clue to the puzzle. 'The Agha appears to be reconsidering his commitment to Aurangzeb's cause,' he murmured under his breath. 'Yesterday, I heard him telling Jafar Khan, "It will be a disaster if he is planning to make Murad Baksh the emperor. If, however, this is only a ruse, then I find such a massive deception distasteful."'

Soon enough we heard that relations between Murad and Aurangzeb had begun to sour, although both brothers were at pains to maintain a façade of filial unity and close friendship. I believe it was Imran Khan who told me of the rumour, one peppered with enough detail for it to be easily true, that the brothers had begun to avoid visiting each other's tents, preferring instead to conduct their confabulations at neutral venues. It seems that the eunuch Shahbaz, Murad's chief adviser, who had no faith in Aurangzeb's promises to his master and constantly warned him of his brother's intentions, decided to take the matter into his own hands.

After the battle at Dharmat and before the armies had resumed their march, the prince had, one evening, accompanied by his son Sultan Muhammad, gone to Murad's tent for dinner. To protect his master, who seemed to be blind to his brother's wiles, Shahbaz had planned to kill the prince and Sultan Muhammad and then take his own life. For this purpose he had asked three armed men loyal to him to hide close to Murad's tent and wait for a signal. While the princes were in conversation, Shahbaz approached Murad, not quite prepared to take the next step without his master's permission.

Looking meaningfully at Murad he asked for permission 'to cut some cloth'. Foolish though he was, Murad realized the import of Shahbaz's words and replied that it was not necessary, but Aurangzeb had already grasped the hidden meaning of the conversation and, making the excuse of a sudden colic attack, hurriedly left for his own camp. He never went to Murad's tent after that, citing the pressure of heavy work as his alibi and would send his son instead.

Unable to resolve the conflict between his duty to the emperor and his belief that the empire would be safer in the hands of Aurangzeb, a conflict sharpened by the doubt my report seemed to have sowed in his mind, Danishmand Khan agonized over his course of action for more than a week and finally decided to remain neutral.

'Let us withdraw into the pleasures of philosophy while the strife rages around us, Bernier,' he said to me with a smile that did not hide the strain he had been through in the last four months. 'We shall stay in Delhi and not join the court in Agra. And you shall unravel for me the mysteries of Descartes's thought, especially his Fourth Discourse. I still cannot comprehend why Descartes says "I think, therefore I am" is the first principle of his philosophy. Why does he say that this was "so certain and so evident that all the most extravagant suppositions of the sceptics were not capable of shaking it"? To me, this seems like the avowal of a believer, not the reasoned conclusion of a philosopher.'

'Stars can be cruel, too, especially those whose fires have begun to die out'

NICCOLAO MANUCCI

THE WINTER OF 1657 was severe. The morning fog hung low, rebuffing until well past noon a pale sun's efforts to break its hold. Even when it did emerge, the sun shone no warmer than a summer moon. A couple of hours of weak warmth in the afternoons merely stirred the cold in our joints without ever dissipating it. By five in the evening it was dark and again bitterly cold. Few people were out in the streets and the bazaars remained deserted. Hapless men huddled around wood-fires trying to blow the sleeping remains of warmth back to life, wringing their hands over the glowing embers to absorb a little heat through the skin before they returned to the chill of their hovels. Even the Omrah, warmly clad in their overcoats and vests lined with sable, felt compelled to complain about the cold as they awaited news on the progress of the rebel princes.

The chill was to keep its hold through the initial months of the following year when a time of eerie calm descended on the empire as factions and forces across the land aligned and realigned in a concerted effort to draft its fate. Although there was no sign of open unrest in the bazaars, or alarm among the nobility, I could sense an air of anticipation hovering uneasily over the city. Away from the familiar routine of my life in Delhi, I spent much of the time wandering Agra's fog-shrouded streets.

For someone who seldom thinks of the past and prefers always to look ahead, I found images from my childhood in Venice becoming frequent companions on my ramblings. This was a rare stabbing of homesickness. The images were not those I remembered with revulsion: the vomit surge of hatred for a brutish father, abject poverty and constant hunger. The memories that returned were of an earlier time, when my mother was still alive and I was the miracle who had turned back the Great Plague. As I walked through Agra's deserted streets at night, I often found myself in Venice on a chilly February night when the city looks its most desolate, and most beautiful. Like most exiles, the images of my longing were of places, not people—of Venice's churches, monasteries and palaces; of the Grand Canal, the fairest and best-built street in the world, its shops stocked with Murano glassware, silks and tapestries. I would cross a misty bridge, follow the twists and turns of a street along dark, silent canals and come out of my trance only to find myself in front of my house in Agra, waiting for a sleepy watchman to open the gate.

For most of February 1658, Prince Dara was in a state of high excitement. The emperor's health, judging from the first faint stirrings of his lust for women, was no longer a cause for anxiety. Yet he showed little eagerness to resume his royal duties. He was content to leave the governance of the empire to the Wali Ahad. Prince Dara assumed that such delegation of royal duties also extended to the execution of wars against his brothers. Here he was mistaken. The crafty old monarch, still protective of the other princes, was busy planning his own moves, beginning with secret instructions to Raja Jai Singh to press the imperial assault against Shuja with less than full vigour.

'All we need is to make that ill-mannered prince realize the folly of his ways and retreat to Bengal. It will be catastrophic if a Mughal prince were killed in battle or, worse, brought to the court in chains as a prisoner,' the emperor had said to the raja.

Once in the field, Sulaiman Shukoh, sharing his father's eagerness for swift and decisive action, had pushed towards Benares by continuous marches. Raja Jai Singh, on the other hand, constantly sought to delay the imperial advance. Puzzled by Jai Singh's lack of dash, and unaware of the emperor's secret instructions, Prince Dara tried flattery.

'With the tongue of divine inspiration,' he wrote, 'His Majesty has said that just as your illustrious ancestor Raja Man Singh conquered and crushed Mirza Hakim, you will crush this unmannerly and luckless wretch. Through visions and books of astrology I have learnt what by divine guidance I firmly believe to be true: that this great victory will be achieved by you, the worthiest of the worthy.'

The Wali Ahad was not naïve. In the stiffness and coldly formal tone of Jai Singh's dispatches, he could sense that the raja's devotion to his cause was less than enthusiastic. Yet, he could not afford to antagonize someone who was not only considered one of the finest generals in the imperial army but also one who exercised considerable influence on other Hindu princes. Even when his son's letter, complaining of Jai Singh's tardy prosecution of the war and expressing doubts regarding the raja's motives, reached his court, Prince Dara did not hesitate to publicly adopt the emperor's position and take Sulaiman to task. 'His Majesty suspects that this must have been written out of enmity,' he replied to his son. 'My son is directed to have the dispatches from the field written by the great raja himself, so that His Majesty can accept them as accurate and authentic.'

At the same time, taking Wazir Khan's advice, he wrote separately to Sulaiman that he should be decisive in pressing his attack and finish with the war as quickly as possible. The message carried a subtle reminder that as a Mogul prince Sulaiman was the commander-in-chief of the imperial forces. He was answerable to no one but his father and the emperor.

To Jai Singh, he wrote: 'His Majesty desires very much that the severed head of that unmannerly wretch (Shuja) be brought to him.' The news of the outcome of the battle reached Agra on the morning of twentieth March 1658. A music recital in the Wali Ahad's mansion welcoming the arrival of spring and featuring the royal musician Azim Khan and the great Hindu singer Ram Bhatt had just ended. I think there were perhaps twenty of us sitting on Persian and Turkish carpets in the central courtyard that day. As a special treat, the women of the harem had been allowed to hear the music from behind stone-latticed windows on the first floor. Sunshine streamed into the courtyard. Having shed its wintery mask, the sun was increasing its warmth with each day that took us towards the arrival of summer. Masses of crimson bougainvillea foamed over the walls. Hot, steaming milk, garnished with crushed pistachios, honey and saffron, was being served in silver tumblers.

Before the recital, the prince had asked Sarmad to sing his favourite poem, which the poet had once dedicated to him. I was glad to see that Sarmad had made a concession for winter by wrapping a rough woollen blanket around his otherwise bare shoulders. As he began his song, the richness of the melody and fullness of the poet's voice filled the air.

'Which is the idol, who the maker?
Who is the lover and who the beloved?
Ask in the church, the temple, the Kaba
And all is silence, all is darkness there.
Yet in the garden where the sunshine glows,
One perfect presence moves in all that grows.
He is the lover, He the beloved,
He is the bramble and He the rose.
Is the heart wise? Then the beloved is there.

Does the eye see? Then it sees Him everywhere.
Does the ear hear? Then all it hears is talk of Him.
Does the tongue speak? Then it lays the secret bare.'

The prince's eyes were moist when Sarmad finished. Even in the middle
of a political crisis, the Wali Ahad's spiritual body did not crawl away
into a dark corner and lock the door behind it. To be fully engaged
in affairs of the state did not mean that he had banished or was no
longer aware of the softer emotions that continued to brush against
his soul with a feathery touch.

Just as the prince rose to embrace Sarmad, we heard excited
shouts from the direction of the gate. Moments later, the captain of
the palace guard rushed into the courtyard, trying hard to reduce his
pace to a dignified stride as he approached the Wali Ahad. Shuffling
behind him, his face a combination of exhaustion and exhilaration
was a man dressed in the dusty green uniform of a messenger among
Prince Dara's guards who had been placed under Sulaiman Shukoh's
command. I watched the prince glow with pride as he listened to the
messenger recounting his son's victory.

Having received his father's last dispatch, Sulaiman had needed
no further encouragement. He reached Benares within two weeks and
had a bridge of boats constructed over the Ganges. Within twenty-four
hours the prince had crossed over to the other side and set up camp.
This was a decisive move since it contested Shuja's hold on the bank
of the river along which ran the great military road, to Shuja's capital,
Rajmahal. Meanwhile, Shuja too had reached the neighbourhood with
his army and fleet. He camped in a well-chosen spot, hidden by a thick
jungle in the front and bordered by the Ganges at the back. Provisioned
by their boats and believing they were immune to an attack through
the jungle, Shuja's army soon relaxed its initial vigilance. Shuja himself
was in the habit of sleeping till noon. His officers, unaccustomed to
the chilly nights of northern India, were less than attentive to their
duty of doing the rounds of pickets at night to keep the sentries alert.
Early in the morning of fourteenth February, Sulaiman, riding at

the head of a select group of mail-clad horsemen, suddenly fell upon Shuja's sleeping camp, scattering the soldiers in all directions. Shuja himself had been lucky to escape to his fleet which immediately set sail, leaving the rest of the fleeing soldiers to be butchered.

At the conclusion of the messenger's report, the prince removed a string of large pink Basra pearls from his own person and pressed it into the messenger's palm. His joy was such that in his haste to reward the bearer of these tidings, the string broke and some of the pearls scattered on the carpet. 'Do not pick a single pearl that has touched the ground. Replace the missing ones with rubies,' he commanded as he embraced the awe-struck messenger.

Publicly, again at the urging of Wazir Khan, the prince awarded to Jai Singh all credit for the victory. In a letter that began with a sacred formula of the Hindus which defines God as 'Satchitanand'—Truth, Consciousness, Bliss—he wrote to the raja, 'You have achieved what even your grandfather Raja Man Singh could not have accomplished. Within the last hundred years no one has been granted such a victory.'

Although still deferential to his father, the Wali Ahad took Shuja's defeat as a sign that his own reign had begun. His bearing became more regal, his mien graver, more imperial.

Soon after this, Prince Dara's favourite astrologer, Bhawani Das, reinforced the prince's conviction of imminent triumph by solemnly presenting, in open court, a signed paper in which he had written that the prince would become the emperor of Hindustan within the next six months. I find myself to be both a believer and a non-believer of astrological predictions. On the one hand, I find it inconceivable that the planets whirling unconcernedly in their heavenly orbits could influence the life of a human being. On the other hand, in India, I have come across predictions, such as the exact date and details of a misfortune or perhaps even a windfall, to be so specific and accurate that they have left me astounded. Undoubtedly, most of the predictions are so general that they can always be interpreted as having come true by a believer who tends to forget all the instances when the astrologer was wrong. Yet, that single, correct prediction will outweigh hundreds that were false, and compel complete faith in astrology.

Bhawani Das was fond of me and visited me often. Perhaps he was simply fond of my wine, which he drank in large quantities. I asked him how he had had the courage to commit himself thus on paper.

'What will happen to you if your prediction does not come true?' I queried.

Deep in the cups, the astrologer laughed heartily. 'Ah, my dear Manucci, if my prediction comes true, the prince will reward me liberally. If not, he will be so busy trying to save his own head that he will not have time to seek mine.'

Perhaps I believed in my friend's prediction more than he did himself. In any event, enthused by the news of Sulaiman Shukoh's victory and the prophecy of the Wali Ahad's ascension to the throne, I was more than determined to hitch my star to Prince Dara's and take an active part in the war.

Since much of my medical practice was in the harems of the nobility which had not yet moved to Agra, I had a good deal of time on my hands and spent my evenings sharing wine with a group of European artillerymen in the emperor's service. For some reason, the Moguls believe that Europeans are naturally gifted in this branch of war which holds little interest for them. To the Moguls, the epitome of real soldiering is a cavalry charge, not a barrage of artillery fire. A true Mogul would any day breathe in the dust from horses' hooves than inhale the smoke of gunfire. When I expressed my enthusiasm in learning the art of firing a gun, they promised to make an artilleryman out of me within a couple of weeks. All I had to do was learn how to aim. All the rest, the raising, lowering, loading and firing of the gun would be done by Indian labourers employed for the purpose.

The Wali Ahad was assembling a vast army and the need had arisen to source all kinds of battlefield skills. Encouraged by my new friends, who said I had made spectacular progress in just over a week, I offered my services to Barqandaz Khan, head of Prince Dara's artillery. Barqandaz had won the prince's favour after he had killed an owl that had taken up its abode in an alcove in the prince's bedroom. The portly general welcomed my proposal since he knew I enjoyed the Wali Ahad's favour and, more so, as I did not ask to be paid anything extra beyond my existing salary. And so it came to be that, as part of the imperial artillery, I was to witness from the closest quarters the battle at Samugarh, fought between the imperial army and the combined forces of Aurangzeb and Murad.

It would not be long before I was to learn that stars can be cruel, too, especially those whose fires have begun to die out, and that fate can betray hopes as easily as it raises them.

Within a month, the mood in the Wali Ahad's court had swung from triumph to gloom. News arrived that the imperial army led by Jaswant Singh and Qasim Khan, the second commander of the imperial army, which had been sent southwards to block the advance of Aurangzeb and Murad, had been defeated. I was not personally present at Dharmat but knew enough officers of the imperial army and European artillerymen in Aurangzeb's service to piece together an accurate account of the battle.

The two armies had faced each other at the opposite ends of the river Sipra, north of Ujjain. It was the dry season when the water flow is minimal and the river is fordable in at least seven places. The river-bed is quite narrow but is littered with stones of all sizes. Its banks are steep, making either descent or ascent considerably difficult. Aurangzeb's plan was to discharge his artillery and allow Murad Baksh and his force to ford the river under the cover of their fire. He had come to a secret understanding with Qasim Khan, the second commander of the imperial army. According to their pact, Qasim Khan would discharge only three volleys for show and then retire. He had already hidden the rest of his powder and shot the previous night.

The battle was fierce. Raja Jaswant Singh and his Rajputs offered furious resistance to Murad, as is their wont. Murad himself fought with great courage. The Rajputs had to give way since Qasim Khan's withdrawal had exposed their flank.

While the news of the defeat demoralized the court, it enraged Prince Dara to such a degree that for the first time he spoke harsh words to his father. 'If your Majesty had only listened to me and not entrusted an army to Mir Jumla, the traitor would not have transferred it to Aurangzeb. You have been too mild to your rebellious sons when severity was needed.' He even demanded that Mir Jumla's children and his wife who had been left at the court as hostages be immediately dealt with—the two sons beheaded, and the wife and daughter sent to a common brothel. The emperor dissuaded him, pointing out that Mir Jumla's collusion with Aurangzeb was an improbability, since it would have exposed his family to grave danger.

'It is the will of Allah, my son,' he said. 'My sins have caught up with me. I deserve it all. But we have work to do, armies to raise and no time to lose in recriminations or in creating new enemies.'

Prince Dara's anger, a fitful affair at best, soon dissipated. He threw himself with great energy into raising one of the largest armies the empire has ever seen. Orders went out to the governors of the northern and western provinces as also to the various Omrah and *mansabdar*s to provide men and weapons for the decisive battle ahead. Messengers were sent to Sulaiman and Raja Jai Singh to immediately conclude a peace deal with Shuja, who had fled to Patna and secured himself in the fort of Munger. They were to then hasten back to reinforce the army that would face the combined forces of Aurangzeb and Murad. Sulaiman Shukoh's expeditionary force was constituted of Prince Dara's best and most loyal officers and soldiers. It was imperative that they reach in time for the battle that would determine the fate of the empire.

'The greatest army ever to have assembled on the plains of Hindustan!'

NICCOLAO MANUCCI

THE IMPERIAL ARMY LEFT Agra an hour after the break of dawn on eighteenth May 1658 to confront the armies of Aurangzeb and Murad. Bhawani Das, the spokesman of the astrologers at Prince Dara's court had asserted that Mars, the planet of war, had never been as favourable in the prince's horoscope as on this day. From the fort, where he had gone to seek his father's blessings, the prince rode to the city gates in a golden chariot drawn by eight grey horses. In the Hindu tradition this was a reminder that he was going to fight demons of unrighteousness—in this unfortunate war they were his own brothers. At the gate, when he was about to mount his magnificent Ceylonese elephant, Fateh Jang, the 'victor in war', towering a few cubits above the Indian species, Prince Dara loudly cried, *'Gharib muaf, maghrur marg* (To the humble, pardon; to the haughty death)'. I could not help but admire my prince who had words of compassion to utter even as he set out for battle.

Although the sun was still far from its zenith, the day promised
to be oppressively hot. The circles of sweat staining my armpits were
rapidly expanding even at that early hour. But the excitement of the
time easily overcame all feelings of discomfort and foreboding. What a
marvellous sight it was to behold the march of the greatest army ever
to have assembled on the plains of Hindustan! There were more than a
hundred thousand cavalry, twenty thousand infantry, a hundred pieces
of field artillery manned by two hundred European artillerymen! Over
five hundred majestic war elephants in armours of shimmering metal,
each carrying two men in its howdah handling a swivel gun that would
fire a ball weighing three to four ounces. And an equal number of camels,
each with a driver and a man on it with a similar gun.

To someone viewing the march from a distance or from a height,
it would have looked like a gigantic wave gently rolling forward.
Different sections of this fluid mass lit up as they caught the rays of
the rising sun. The reflecting surfaces were many: Prince Dara's gold-
plated howdah, the steel chains on the trunks of elephants and the
broad cutlasses of Damascus steel affixed to their tusks with rings, the
polished armour of squadrons of Rajput cavalry that escorted Prince
Dara, the heads of the riders' lances that were a myriad pinpoints of
shifting light.

To an uninformed observer, it may have seemed that the imperial
army was a relentless storm that would sweep away any resistance
standing in its way. But its appearance belied the reality. A large
number of the soldiers were butchers, barbers, blacksmiths, tailors
and ordinary citizens who had been newly enlisted to swell the
volume of the imperial forces. Suitably armed and mounted on horses
they looked impressive enough, but most knew nothing of warfare. I
would be surprised if even a tenth among them had the heart for battle.
Hundreds of shopkeepers, water-carriers, scavengers and others had
been enlisted to supply essentials to the vast army, which was almost
twice the size of the combined troops of the rebel princes.

Ironically, the greatest unknown was the commitment given
by some of the key Omrah to the prince's cause. No one was certain

about whose loyalty had been cajoled or bought by which rebel prince. Treachery during battle was the real possibility. The crafty Emperor Shah Jahan had sensed this better than the good-natured prince, whose spiritual explorations had made him more optimistic about human nature than his cynical father. While his nature made him loveable, it also left him acutely vulnerable. Initially, the emperor had offered to lead the army knowing well that any noble contemplating betrayal during battle would pause before taking his first step towards treachery if the emperor himself was in command.

At the time, Khalilullah Khan had vigorously opposed the suggestion. 'His Majesty is aged and infirm,' he had said. 'If, God forbid, something happens to him during the march in this heat or, even worse, during battle, the troops will be completely demoralized. The risk is not worth taking, especially since our numbers and the Wali Ahad's courage assure us an easy victory.'

When Princess Jahanara, genuinely worried about her father's health, supported Khalilullah's advice, the emperor had reluctantly agreed to let his son take the lead.

I have it on the good authority of Hakim Tabinda that when Prince Dara went to the fort to take leave of his father and sister on the eve of the march, the three had cried from an excess of emotion.

The emperor had been the first to regain control. 'My son,' he said. 'Your father hoped to see you become king peacefully, but who can fathom the secrets of the Almighty. I had hoped to go forth myself against those rebels, Aurangzeb and Murad, both unworthy of being my sons or your brothers. But you had compassion on my years and illness. I consent to stay back as you wish but entreat you, my beloved son, to avoid battle till Sulaiman Shukoh arrives. You will increase your chances of victory manifold once you have him by your side. I pray that you are victorious and that you become the emperor of Hindustan. I place you in the hands of Allah.' He had proceeded to embrace Prince Dara and sprinkle drops of rose attar on his shoulders.

Jahanara Begum had pressed her worn copy of Rumi's poems, bound in crimson velvet and fraying at the edges, with her seal embossed in gold on the cover, in her brother's hands. 'We have often read this together, my dearest brother. It has accompanied us on our path. May it bring you solace, and peace to your mind, even in the turmoil of war,' she had said.

At noon the army halted eight miles south of Agra on an unbroken plain of uncultivated land. By sunset, the camp was an enchanting town magically created out of air in the wilderness. Beautiful tents in every colour of the rainbow, flying flags of all shapes, colours and sizes, were spread all over the site. It was well past eight in the evening when the last groups of infantry straggled in and the last cooking fires were lit. At night, the camp had a festive air. Soldiers wandered around the camp looking for old comrades. Groups of men gathered together to break into impromptu songs and the ambience was suffused with camaraderie and merriment. Delectable smells of the preparation of food from different parts of India, each with its unique mix of spices, wafted through the air. I was thankful for the warm breeze that blew over the land. The strong smell of cooked spices, combined with that of the sweat of horses, camels, elephants and men, would otherwise have been intolerable.

Instead of resting in my tent in the area allotted to European artillerymen, I decided to walk across to the neighbouring camp set up by Ram Singh Rathor and his men. Ram Singh was a Rajput prince whose fifteen thousand horsemen were the designated left wing of the imperial army. My choice was dictated by curiosity as much as by restiveness. Late in the afternoon, perhaps an hour before sunset, still groggy from sleep, I had been awakened by the sound of horses' hooves. Coughing from the dust that had blown into my tent, I had looked out to see squadrons of Rajput horsemen cantering away in a southerly direction. I wanted to find out why.

A group of about a dozen Rajput officers was squatting in a circle outside Ram Singh's tent finishing their frugal dinner of *chapati*s made from millet, a cooked vegetable and lentil gruel. Seeing me approach, the Rajput prince invited me to join them. A young man, less than thirty years of age, Ram Singh possessed the lean and hawk-like look characteristic of his race: chiselled features, large, expressive eyes, long black hair curling over a crimson *qaba*, and a moustache with upturned ends presiding over full lips and a strong chin. I had tied my *qaba* on the right side as is the fashion of the Muslims while the Hindus fasten theirs on the left. On the other hand, I had shaved my beard and wore a moustache like the Rajputs. Ram Singh and his officers were puzzled by my appearance and asked me which faith I ascribed to. I told them I was Christian, a revelation that prompted queries about whether I was a Muslim Christian or Hindu Christian, since they were unaware about religions other than the ones that predominated in Hindustan. I seized the opportunity to enlighten the raja on our faith, but it soon became apparent that though he listened politely the prince could not comprehend the essentials of Christianity any more than his officers could.

Quickly abandoning the topic, I enquired about the movements of the horsemen whom I had seen departing the camp a short while ago. As it turned out, they were reinforcements dispatched to secure the crossings of the river Chambal. The Chambal was completely dry at this time of the year but because of the profusion of stones, boulders and hollow craters on its bed it still presented a significant obstacle. Aurangzeb's and Murad's armies were yet to reach the opposite bank and the strategy was to take up positions on that side to deny the rebels a crossing until Sulaiman Shukoh's forces joined the imperial army. We were to then mount an overwhelming offensive.

From the time I had joined the group I had noticed that the barber attached to the raja's retinue, sitting a few feet away from the men, was preparing opium. The wiry, middle-aged man with unshaven, sunken cheeks and wearing a turban too big for his head went about his task with the solemnity of a priest offering our Saviour's blood at the end of Mass. He ground the balls of cooked and dried opium in a mortar and mixed the powder with water in a large marble bowl, agitating the mixture with a pestle. The blend was passed through a strainer and the resulting drops of vermillion liquid collected in a silver bowl.

Sudhir Kakar

The Rajputs' habit of ingesting opium, especially before battle, is well known. It is said the drug makes them even more fearless than is already the nature of their race. More important, being a coagulant, opium prevents excessive blood loss from a wound. In times of peace, opium is taken in small quantities as an aphrodisiac; a large dose will only make a man fall asleep. I know this from a mortifying personal experience I had at one of my favourite brothels in Agra, where I had once been offered opium by the sprightly madam of the house.

'Why are you *farangis* always in a rush?' she had said, calling up a well-rehearsed coquetry in her voice and gestures. 'Sit for a while with an older woman and experience other joys than those of sleeping with a young one.'

I smoked one pipe with her as we chatted amiably. I felt alert and full of confidence, suddenly aware of an exquisite, relaxed feeling spreading through my limbs. Foolishly, I smoked another pipe while I lay naked in bed waiting for the girl I had selected for the night. The next thing I remember is waking up the following afternoon from a stuporous slumber on a sofa in the ante-chamber of the establishment. My clothes, neatly folded, were lying on a small wooden table next to the sofa. Mortified, I had left the brothel in a hurry to the accompaniment of the girls' giggles.

Now on the battlefield, all conversation had stopped among the group once the barber finished preparing the opium. He ladled some of the liquid into a small silver cup and offered it to the prince with both hands. Ram Singh sprinkled a few drops on the palm of his right hand and raised it to his forehead as a devout offering to the deity of his clan. He then gulped down the liquid with a loud slurping noise and passed the cup back to the barber to be refilled. Since I was a guest, the opium was first offered to me and then distributed to others according to their rank. Each man took the bowl reverentially in his palms and made the same loud sound as they drank the concoction, perhaps to show it honour.

Opium has a bitter taste and, unlike Muslims, the Rajputs do not disguise the taste of opium by adding nutmeg, cinnamon, saffron or ambergris. They believe that the more bitter the taste the greater is the efficacy of the intoxicant. Except for a slight feeling of relaxation, the drinking of opium did not affect me as strongly as its smoking had done in the brothel. I believe it is as much the ritual partaking of opium before battle as its properties as a drug that makes Rajputs such fierce fighters.

War, I was to discover, had nothing to do with my childish notions of it being honourable combat. What decides a battle is not the courage of the soldiers or the enterprise of the generals but treason's secret knife and a traitor's hidden rage. I have remained haunted by the questions: Was there something in Prince Dara's character that attracted treachery? Was betrayal foretold by his life's star?

Some of the traitors were, of course, inherited. Shaista Khan and Khalilullah Khan were his father's poisoned gifts, men who had waited long for an opportunity to avenge unbearable humiliations. But Qasim Khan, Champat Rai, Malik Jivan, the astrologer Bhawani Das? Were they just weak men who succumbed to Aurangzeb's blandishments, selling out their sovereign for a foreign purse? Odd as it may sound, I believe the source of their treachery lay in Prince Dara's goodness, which failed to discern the false dissembling guile in their amity and their oaths. The compassionate prince had pardoned so much treachery that the traitors were sanguine that they would never have to pay its price with the dear blood of their bodies. A wise king must and should have forgiveness in him, but he must never forgive treason. *That* should be rued, not just with tears but with blood.

Betrayal was Prince Dara's lot from the very first day on the field. Reports had reached him that Aurangzeb had commanded his generals to attack the imperial forces with the full force of their cavalry, without delay, before Sulaiman Shukoh arrived to join his father. We did not know that the speech was a ploy to make the imperial army take up a defensive position and that it had been cleverly leaked to us.

Too late, we discovered that not all crossings of the Chambal had been secured. Twelve leagues upstream, a crossing in the territory of Champat Rai Bundela had remained unguarded. A robber chieftain who had once been caught and imprisoned by a Mogul viceroy and owed his life to Prince Dara, Champat Rai had assured the prince that under no circumstance would he allow Aurangzeb to ford the river from his territory. The crafty Aurangzeb had, however, managed to buy the chieftain's loyalty with valuable gifts and promises of even greater rewards in the future and gained access to the crossing. He had crossed the river with eight thousand horsemen, leaving the bulk of his army behind. Our forces that stood guard with guns and arrows and spears at ferry points downstream had been completely taken by surprise.

Enraged, Prince Dara railed against Champat Rai's perfidy.

'What can you expect from someone who is a robber putting on the airs of a Rajput noble?' Rao Chatrasal, one of the Rajput princes in his service said.

'A fox pretending to be a tiger,' Ram Singh Rathor concurred. 'His mother was a slave girl in his father's harem.'

Prince Dara wanted to attack Aurangzeb without delay before the entire rebel army forded the river. Ibrahim Khan, a twenty-three-year-old Mogul, who, despite his youth, was one of the best generals of the imperial army, offered to take twelve thousand horsemen and throw the rebels back into the river. In his verve and dash, he reminded me of the Wali Ahad's son Sulaiman. The Wali Ahad was inclined to sanction this bold initiative but Khalilullah took the prince to one side and advised him against the move.

'The credit for the victory will go to Ibrahim Khan, Your Highness, and not to you. Ibrahim Khan is young and inexperienced in matters of war. If we detach twelve thousand horsemen from our force, we will weaken it. The victory that is now assured will become doubtful.'

Prince Dara's hesitation in promptly launching an offensive proved costly. By next morning, when the army moved to block the rebels, it was too late. Aurangzeb's forces had crossed the river and were entrenching themselves in a vast plain outside the village of Samugarh.

The distance between the two armies was now less than a league and a half. The prince was still of a mind to immediately attack Aurangzeb's forces which were exhausted from the crossing. Some of the rebels' heavier guns were still on the other side of the river. But the traitors again prevailed. This time they succeeded in bribing Bhawani Das to convince the prince that neither the day nor the hour was astrologically favourable. Prince Dara hesitated again.

On the same evening the prince received a letter from the emperor who had got news of Aurangzeb's crossing of the Chambal. The emperor instructed Prince Dara to retreat and take up position outside Agra till the arrival of Sulaiman Shukoh. This was an impossible demand. If we retreated, Aurangzeb would advance with greater speed and with lifted spirits. Our army would lose confidence in its commander and desert in large numbers.

'Your Majesty should ease your heart,' Prince Dara wrote back to his father. 'I have decided to attack tomorrow. Within three days I promise to drag those wretches, Aurangzeb and Murad Baksh, bound into your august presence. You may then punish them as you deem fit.'

On the morning of twenty-seventh May, the day the prince wanted to commence battle, there was an unseasonable shower. It cooled the earth and brought relief to the soldiers. Judging from the trumpeting of the elephants and the bellowing of the camels, the animals welcomed it just as much as the men did. The traitors, in collusion with the dog Bhawani Das, now took yet another step to scuttle the Wali Ahad's chances of victory. Knowing well that Aurangzeb's ranks were not in full battle order, they put up the astrologer to counsel the Wali Ahad that the time was not favourable for an attack. 'The skies have been weeping over your defeat, O Prince, from the time they learnt Your Highness wanted to fight today. Tomorrow is the auspicious day on which you will without doubt be victorious. You must rest today.'

Khalilullah Khan, who had accompanied Bhawani Das to ensure the success of their devious plan, supported the astrologer. 'Tomorrow is certainly most auspicious,' he said. 'It is the day the Almighty created light.'

The shadow side of a spiritual person is his conviction that the universe is teeming with signs and portents waiting to be known. Everything is not only interconnected but also has a hidden meaning which can be deciphered by those in possession of *ilm-ruhani*—spiritual knowledge. The Wali Ahad was highly credulous where warnings of astrologers, sorcerers and other practitioners of the occult were concerned. The attack was postponed.

At midnight, three artillery shots were heard being fired from the direction of Aurangzeb's camp. In a few minutes we heard the galloping and neighing of horses, and loud commands, as Prince Dara, accompanied by a few horsemen holding aloft flaming torches, approached our camp on his black Arab stallion. He wanted to personally oversee the firing of three return shots from our largest field gun, a twenty-pounder. I began to dismantle my tent to clear a passage for the prince and his escort so that they did not have to veer a couple of hundred yards to the left where there was a gap large enough for them to pass through. The prince seemed cheerful and waited patiently while the servants untied the ropes that tethered the tent to wooden pegs hammered into the ground.

'We shall soon be back in our beloved Delhi, Manucci,' he said with a smile. 'You can go back to your life of being a doctor, and bleeding the lovely ladies!'

'Your Highness, too, can continue his studies,' I replied.

'Ah, I doubt that, Manucci,' he said. 'It will not be like before. The responsibilities of the throne will not leave me much time to fulfil the obligation to the soul.' He leaned forward and patted his horse's neck as it whinnied and shivered its haunches. 'See, how eager he is to be in the thick of the action,' he said, his voice tinged with pride. 'Just like his master.'

As he rode away the prince appeared calm and full of hope, briefly dissipating the abject foreboding that had not left me since we had marched out of Agra.

Seeing that putting up my tent again would not be worth the time and effort, I mounted my horse and rode out of the camp in the

direction of the enemy army. This was my first war and I was naturally
curious, but, more than that, I needed purposeful physical activity to
allay my returning sense of unease.

The sky was clear and the moon nearly full. The night was
heavy with the swell of piled-up heat. A slight breeze brought in a
most disagreeable reek of faecal matter. I had encountered the stink
wherever the army had halted and found it utterly unbearable. The
higher officers of the army slept with their faces covered with muslin
scarves dipped in rose or jasmine attar, and even appointed a servant
to sprinkle a few drops of the perfume on the cloth every hour through
the night. Although more than four hundred scavengers accompanied
the imperial army to remove horse, camel and elephant dung from
the camp, they could do nothing to eradicate the smell of flatulence
produced by thousands of animals confined to an area of a large village
or a small town. The worst stench came from the surrounding fields
where thousands of ordinary soldiers relieved themselves. As the day
heated up and the sun began to stir the piles of excrement spread over
the land, the stench became overwhelming. When I had commented
on the overpowering odour on my first day on the field I was told that
the fields around the marching route of an army remain uncultivable
for months. Except, that is, for fields that grow brinjals, since the
vegetables prefer this particular manure and can grow to twice their
normal size when supplied with the correct proportions. The price of
brinjals reduced substantially after an army has passed through the
area, although an upper-caste Hindu would never let the vegetable
enter his kitchen.

After riding through a mile of unploughed fields, I reached a
hillock overlooking a deserted village which afforded a clear view
in all directions. Dismounting, I tied my horse to a stately banyan
tree and climbed on to a low, sturdy branch. For about an hour, all
was quiet except for the occasional howl of an abandoned village
dog and the coarse croaking of frogs from the ponds below the hill.
Of this concerted bass chorus that filled the air, one could only say
that the harmony was tolerable but the melody atrocious. More dogs

had begun to bark now. I looked around for signs of movement and watched in dismay as at least a hundred horsemen left our camp in ones and twos and passed close to the village below me as they rode in the direction of Aurangzeb's lines. I waited in silence to see what would transpire. At daybreak, when the sullen orange eye of the moon had still not vanished but glimmered balefully above the horizon, I saw Aurangzeb's army advancing in my direction at a leisurely pace. It became clear to me now that the gunshots we had heard the previous night had been a signal to the traitors that Aurangzeb was ready to give battle at daybreak.

I watched, silent and immobile, as the enemy proceeded. In the front were five divisions of cavalry that were strung out in a wide arc. I estimated each of them at ten thousand horsemen. They were armed with lances, bows and arrows, and matchlocks. Aurangzeb was seated on the elephant in the middle. The cavalry division of Murad Baksh was on his extreme left. Murad Baksh, too, was seated on an elephant that was larger than his brother's. His three-year-old son was sitting in his lap. After the army had passed the village, the cavalry halted. From behind them, the artillery emerged to take up positions in the front, followed by musketeers and camels carrying swivel guns. The morning sun had begun to dissolve the darkness. The sky was becoming lighter, with the last of the surviving stars rapidly fading away. Clambering down the hill, I mounted my horse and rode back to our lines.

The orders for the imperial army to move must have come soon after I left. I saw it had moved forward and Prince Dara had begun to array it for battle. The prince's own division, with his artillery taking up position in the front, was in the middle of our massive force. Each gun carriage flew the scarlet pennant of the Wali Ahad. The guns were chained together to prevent the enemy's horses from riding through the gaps between them and falling on the gunners. The rows of guns protected ten thousand musketeers and five hundred camel-riders with swivel guns. These were followed by armour-clad elephants and twenty-eight thousand horsemen. Prince Dara, mounted on Fateh Jang, was at the rear of his cavalry. He was followed by more elephants carrying drums and trumpets. To the immediate right of the prince's division, under the command of Ram Singh Rathor, were fifteen thousand Rajputs armed with lethal spears and dressed in yellow robes under their chain-mail, which signified their readiness to sacrifice their lives. Next to them, on the extreme right, was Khalilullah, leading thirty thousand Mogul horsemen. To Prince Dara's left was Rustam Khan, the trusted general who had accompanied the prince on his expedition at Kandahar, with fifteen thousand horsemen. To Rustam Khan's left was Rao Chatrasal leading another fifteen thousand horsemen, Rajput as well as Pathan. As the sun rose, dawn began to glint dully on the steel of the spear points and the bronze-iron gun barrels.

When I now think of the army positioned for battle, the ranks are more organized in my imagination than they were in reality. The cavalry divisions, for instance, were not separated by any distance, but were positioned very close to each other, like pine trees in a forest. There was considerable mingling among horses and riders at the edges. Scattered horsemen carrying messages from commanders galloped in front of the massed force. Water-carriers walked to and fro through the lines, stilling thirst on what promised to be the hottest day that year. At around eight o'clock an order was passed from one division to the next that all the courier horsemen should ride back to their respective divisions, and the water-carriers and hawkers retire to the rear of the army, as the artillery was ready to fire. I reached for my gun just as the artillery barrage started. A Mogul horseman who was late in returning to his squadron was hit by a stray ball and was the first casualty. Miraculously, the horse survived, and I watched him limping on alone, yelped at by one of the village dogs. As my eyes turned to the cur, oblivious to the massed death surrounding him, I felt the first stabbing of fear. Unbidden images of my lifeless body lying under a heap of corpses flashed through my mind. Then another image, that of my mother, never as clearly recollected as at that instant, replaced the earlier ones of death and decay. She was lifting up an infant in her arms, a faint smile on her inclined face. I looked up to scan the heavens for a sign that I would not die on a foreign battlefield, far from the canals and bridges of my beloved Venice. High above, I saw the first vultures begin to circle. I knew then with a certainty that can only arise from the depths of one's body and never from the cogitations of the mind that I was not intended to be a part of the feast that awaited them.

With no order to cease fire coming forth, the artillery salvos continued for three hours. The enemy, however, held their fire, except for occasional shots from two or three guns, fired almost as a mockery of our bombardments. As I came to know later, our shots did no damage, for they fell short of Aurangzeb's forces.

When the order to cease fire finally came, the soldiers lay down their weapons and took off the metal head-pieces and the jackets of mail, looking as though they had emerged from an oven kept at low heat. They sought the smallest bits of shade in the wavering shadows thrown by the horses and the lines of guns. As water-carriers swarmed through the lines, I too found refuge from the sun in the shadow thrown by the gun on my left. The casing of my own gun had cracked after the third round of firing. Luckily no one was injured since the crack was detected in time and the gun did not burst. A five-pounder that had burst its barrel while being fired had killed its Belgian gunner and his three helpers, and injured ten others, a few minutes later. It had been scarcely thirty paces to my right. Even ten paces closer and the shards of flying metal would have seriously injured or even maimed me for life. The inchoate feeling of being kept safe from harm that had begun to take hold of me with the image of my mother's face now became a certainty: I was invulnerable.

I heard later that Prince Dara had conferred with his generals during the pause. Khalilullah's advice had been to attack. 'The invincible Wali Ahad is in sight of a famous victory. Without losing a single man, except a wretched horseman who died of heat stroke, your artillery has destroyed a greater part of the enemy. Now it is time to make the final effort and attack.'

The other senior general Rustam Khan, who was reputed to be physically as powerful as Murad and carried a volume of the Persian poet Hafiz's poems in the pocket of his tunic to every battle, differed. He counselled prudence. 'It is better to await the enemy's attack. And attack it must since it has travelled a great distance to seek us. When the attack comes we can take advantage of our valour and our organized positions.'

'I am astonished that so famous a captain should say at this juncture that we should be cowards,' Khalilullah had retorted. 'That we should have so little courage as not to take the offensive after we have almost destroyed the enemy.'

Since defence lacks the glory of attack, Prince Dara found Khalilullah's advice congenial to his own temperament. Rustam Khan was ordered to return to his division and prepare to launch the offensive on a signal from the Wali Ahad.

Barely ten minutes later, the drums began to beat again, signalling a fresh attack. The guns were unchained to allow the troops to pass through the lines. The prince too had set his own elephant in motion. There was much disorder as the non-combatants, the barbers, shopkeepers, water-carriers and the rest began to run in the opposite direction to escape the approaching armies. One of the water-carriers dropped his leather sack full of water and stopped for a moment, agonizing whether he should pick up the sack before deciding that he could run much faster without the load.

From my vantage position in the front row of the guns that were now silent, I could now fully concentrate on watching the battle that began with four squadrons of Prince Dara's cavalry charging at the enemy ranks. As the Omrah leading the attack spurred their horses on to full speed, bright sunlight raking the animals' flanks with fire, the tassels of yak tails in the front and back of the saddles, as well as on the horses' heads, flew about in the wind as though the animals had grown wings.

At first the rebel forces did not react. Then, suddenly, when the horsemen were almost upon them, they discharged their cannon, musketry and swivel pieces. The advancing troops suffered heavy losses and scattered in all directions. From the top of his elephant, Prince Dara signalled for the guns to be moved forward and for the musketeers to advance, but we knew the artillery would be useless at such close quarters. Rustam Khan and Rao Chatrasal, whose divisions too had suffered heavy losses from enemy firing, rallied their troops. Prince Dara now launched an attack with such violence and vigour that he broke through the rebels' frontline artillery. The enemy's camels and infantry were put to flight. Seeing the prince's success at the centre, Aurangzeb sent squadrons of cavalry as reinforcement. The fighting was fierce. Arrows flew thick in the air. We rejoiced to see that the rebel reinforcements were in disarray. Aurangzeb, who was not far away, was in obvious danger if the advance continued from our end, for he was left with few fresh troops. He had even double-chained the legs of his tusker to prevent the animal from suddenly retreating.

But Prince Dara halted to regroup his forces. During this pause he received the news that both Rustam Khan and Rao Chatrasal had been killed, though their forces continued to fight valiantly. The prince veered to the left to reinforce these forces, unwisely evacuating his position at the centre. He fought so valiantly that the rebels were routed. Victorious on three fronts, our morale now rose and every soldier on the field was enthused into fighting with redoubled energy.

Meanwhile, fresh reports reached the prince from the other end of the battlefield. The Rajputs led by Ram Singh Rathor had engaged Murad Baksh's division and had pressed their attack with such energy that they had dispersed Murad's vanguard and captured his guns. A dozen Rajputs led by Ram Singh himself had reached the elephant on which Murad was seated. They let loose arrows at the howdah, killing the driver and planting one in Murad's cheek, just under the left eye. Murad was a lout, but a brave man. He did not retreat. Even though he was trying to control the elephant at the same time as he was saving himself from the relentless shower of arrows, he picked up his son, threw the boy on the floor of the howdah and covered him with a shield on which he placed his foot. On seeing Murad in dire straits, Ram Singh and his Rajputs dismounted and leapt on to the elephant. They hoped to sever its girths by sword cuts and thus bring Murad to ground. But the Rajputs' luck had finally run out. One of Murad's arrows struck Ram Singh in the chest, felling him, and Murad's expertly trained war elephant seized the body with its trunk and threw it under its feet, crushing the brave Rajput. When Prince Dara heard the news, he hastened to reinforce the Rajputs and capture the exposed Murad. What unfolded now was the final act of Khalilullah Khan's treachery.

As a part of our battle strategy, Khalilullah was supposed to have held his division in reserve to aid the imperial army in sectors where its situation became precarious. After the warning I had received from his wife, I had tried to keep an eye on Khalilullah's movements on the battlefield and had seen no sign that his division was fulfilling its assigned role. In the beginning, his forces had discharged several volleys of arrows but as soon he saw Rao Chatrasal's men engage with the enemy, he had commanded his own men to retire behind the line of battle. In spite of their losses from artillery and musket fire, the brave Rajputs and Pathans had driven themselves in like a steel wedge between Aurangzeb's troops and Murad's. All I saw of Khalilullah's mercenaries was scattered groups aimlessly galloping from one end of the battlefield to another with loud shouts of '*Ba-kush! Ba-kush!*'

Much later, I was told by the captain of Prince Dara's bodyguard that Khalilullah had come up to the prince and said, 'I have been in many wars, waged many campaigns, my prince, but I have never seen such a valiant commander as you. Only one thing now remains: the capture of Aurangzeb. Once you have done that, your name will go down in the history of the dynasty of Timur with the same honour as its founder. Let us not lose this opportunity. Aurangzeb is being pressed by Chatrasal's Rajputs who are eager to avenge the death of their chief. Descend from your elephant and mount your horse so that we can quickly seize Aurangzeb. I have kept my troops fresh especially for this purpose.'

All I could see from afar was the prince alight from Fateh Jang and mount his horse. Even I, a foreigner, fighting my first war in an alien land, knew how fatal such a move would be. In India, soldiers do not fight for a cause, a nation or a country, but for their leader. If the leader is killed or flees from battle, they immediately lose heart. Each man then becomes intent only on saving himself. All through the battle, the soldiers and their commanders had continued to keep an eye on the Wali Ahad's elephant. Seeing the howdah suddenly empty, they presumed he was dead. Confusion reigned in the imperial army and in the midst of the chaos Khalilullah revealed his true colours. He joined Aurangzeb and turned on his own comrades. I could only watch in dismay as the once supreme army scattered in all directions like a dark cloud blown by a high wind. It was not a defeat, but a rout. And, as if to underline the fact that Aurangzeb was fortune's favourite, a searing loo began to blow, enveloping the battlefield in a squall of dust. Cut off from their sources of water, thousands in the imperial army perished from thirst. The battle of Samugarh and, with it, the war for the Peacock Throne was over.

*'Betrayal, which had been quietly tiptoeing
into the prince's fate, had now taken
full possession of it'*

NICCOLAO MANUCCI

RAGE, RAGE THE COLOUR of blood, washed over me. Rage over the blackest treachery that had reduced our once glorious army to a rabble in headlong flight. Hues of red abounded, every shade of it, wherever I looked: the baleful crimson of the afternoon sun seen through the cloud of whirling dust, the scarlet red of clotted blood on the manes and sides of wounded horses left to die in the gutted fields.

I rode my mare hard, without a second look at the stragglers on foot, bent double against the hot wind blowing in their faces, coughing from the sand in their mouths, their tongues thick, lips scabbed. I closed my mind to the wounded who could no longer walk but lay on the ground gasping for breath. I rode ahead, past corpses of men and animals that lay scattered over the leagues of scrubby ground between Samugarh and Agra. Flocks of vultures surrounded the remains, renting to pieces their gory prey. Carrion crows circled overhead, the intrepid among them darting down to snatch at exposed entrails and carry them in triumph to a kikar tree, to then peck unhurriedly on a bloody twine trailing from a thorny branch. The defeated limped ahead, singly or in small groups, their horses stumbling, torn banners trampled into the ruddy sand, having discarded all except the essentials for flight—their miserable lives and footwear for their bloody feet.

I arrived in Agra at around ten at night and made straight for the home of my friend Hakim Tabinda, who was sure to have the latest news. He told me it had just been three hours since Prince Dara had arrived and set up camp outside the city, fearful that he might get trapped if Aurangzeb were to lay siege upon it. As news of the defeat trickled in from the late afternoon, the city, Tabinda said, had turned into a charnel house of mourning. Loud lamentations had been heard from the emperor's apartments in the fort, which were echoed and amplified by the wails that gradually arose from the streets, the bazaars and the dwellings of humble citizens.

The prince had been so ashamed of his defeat that he had made no attempt to meet his father after he arrived in Agra. To the emperor's request for a last meeting with his beloved son, he had replied, 'Give up your wish to see my abashed face again. I only beg Your Majesty's benediction on this distracted and half-dead man for the long journey he has before him.'

The monarch had sent back a message of consolation: 'An army is still intact in the east under the command of my grandson Sulaiman Shukoh. There is no room for despair, my son. Raise another army to reverse the fortunes of war.' The message was accompanied by mules carrying sacks laden with gold coins and an order for the governor of Delhi to allow the Wali Ahad access to the city and the emperor's treasury. Princess Jahanara too had sent him precious jewels with a message expressing her love and the hope that one day she would see him ascend the Peacock Throne.

People milled about, hungry for news of how the battle had been lost. I had passed Khalilullah Khan's mansion on my way through the city, and when an old woman emerged to enquire if I knew what had happened to their master, I had replied that I had seen Khalilullah lying dead on his back in the battlefield, a spear thrust into his chest, his arms tossed wide. 'And a vulture was gouging out his eyes,' I added spitefully, still furious over his vile treachery. The old woman had rushed inside weeping loudly, and I had felt greatly satisfied at the sounds of lamentation that emanated from the traitor's house.

I would have joined the prince that very night except that my mare was so worn out it could hardly stand. I decided to rest for the night and look for the Wali Ahad the following day. But the next morning when Tabinda shook me awake he informed me that the prince had hurriedly set forth for Delhi before dawn. He was accompanied by his wife Nadira Begum, his children and grandchildren, and an escort of five hundred horsemen, most of them slaves in his household.

It was a wise decision, for by the time the sun had climbed to midheaven, squadrons of Aurangzeb's cavalry had scattered themselves along the road from Agra to Delhi, blocking access to Prince Dara's suspected sympathizers in the city who might have contemplated joining the fleeing prince. I had little choice but to remain in Agra and continue to be an impotent witness to the vile designs of the fiend princes, who arrived four days later with their armies and set up camp next to the Taj Mahal, across the river from the fort.

Even before the battle of Samugarh, Aurangzeb had many secret sympathizers among the Omrah. He had, in fact, deputed his maternal uncle Shaista Khan to persuade the others to desert the Wali Ahad and the emperor. Shaista Khan, who loathed Emperor Shah Jahan, rightly seeing in him the agent of his wife's dishonour and demise, was successful in persuading most nobles to embrace Aurangzeb's cause. After Aurangzeb's victory, it was pathetic to see the alacrity with which the few remaining waverers changed their allegiance. The only ones to hold out till the end and declare their neutrality even after the victorious armies marched into Agra were the foreign minister

Danishmand Khan, and my friend, the emperor's personal physician, Mukarram Khan, both natives of Persia.

The emperor thus had little hope left of winning over the generals to his side. He could still have ventured out of the fort and into the city in an effort to rally the citizenry behind the throne. If this were Europe, such an outpouring of support for the emperor could have caused the interlopers considerable headache. But this is India. Indians are loveable, but too meek and cowed down for such spirited deeds. They are always ready to complain, but rarely to act. They will shed copious tears of sympathy on the misfortune of their king but will not come out on the street to avenge his humiliation.

What the cunning emperor could not achieve by force he now decided to accomplish through wiles. But Aurangzeb was more than his match in devious ploys. The day after his arrival, Aurangzeb sent his trusted eunuch Itbar Khan to his father with a message. Shorn of Persian floweriness and Mogul ornamentation, the message said: 'I am elated at the good news of your recovery. No one is sorrier than I that Dara's ambition and evil intentions forced me to take the extreme step of going to war in which so many Mughals lost their lives. I am now in Agra, eager to receive and obey your orders.'

The emperor sent back *his* eunuch with the message: 'Who knows his children better than their father? I have always been wary of the evil nature and small capacity of Dara Shukoh. I am delighted by your arrival and as a sign of the love I bear you, I am pleased to grant you all the territories of the Deccan. My longing to embrace you is great. I want to converse with you in person on how we should address the disorder convulsing the empire.'

The monarch's plan was to lure Aurangzeb to the fort and set the emperor's personal guard of three thousand Tartar and Uzbek women, strong of limb and skilled in the use of arms, upon him on his arrival. Aurangzeb sensed that a trap was being set for him—in his father's situation, he would have acted no differently—and repeatedly postponed his visits with many excuses. Once Aurangzeb's control over Agra was complete, he instructed his son Sultan Muhammad to encircle the fort. The emperor had no choice but to prepare for a siege and made rounds of the fort encouraging the garrison to stand firm in the fight that lay ahead of them. He was unaware that Aurangzeb had already gained control of the commanders through bribes and threats. Within the next three days, most of the soldiers had deserted the fort.

Aurangzeb sent his father a new message: 'I have been ill. In my absence my restless soldiers acted on their own initiative. I would like to send my son with my apologies and humble respects. Once I am restored to health, I will hasten to present myself in person.'

Hoping that his grandson's visit was a precursor to Aurangzeb's own appearance at the fort, the emperor gave his assent. But, as soon as the gates opened, Sultan Muhammad rushed in with a company of his soldiers, killing everyone who sought to bar his way. Emperor Shah Jahan was in his harem when he heard the uproar outside. A cautious and deliberate man, Aurangzeb had asked his son to halt at the harem's gate and have a message delivered to the monarch: 'Your Majesty should take your ease in the harem. You are not well enough to rule. I shall relieve you of the weight of the empire and take it on my own shoulders.'

The desperate emperor now played his last card. He sent a message to his grandson saying that he found Sultan Muhammad to be such an able and brave young man that he wanted to crown his grandson the emperor of Hindustan. But Sultan Muhammad refused to discuss such a proposal. 'My orders are to take possession of keys to the fort and nothing else,' he replied roughly. Then he stationed his guards outside the harem with strict instructions and left. When, after a day or so, the emperor realized that the harem's food supplies had been cut off, he capitulated and handed over all the keys and weapons to his grandson. He was now confined to the harem, along with Princess Jahanara, their female slaves and a trusted eunuch. Roshanara Begum, Aurangzeb's younger sister and ally, was installed in a palace in the city with much pomp. The harem was fenced with wickets and gates, and guarded by strapping young female sentries. The emperor could neither write to nor speak with anyone outside the harem, or for that matter even enjoy a stroll in the garden, without the permission of the eunuch Itbar Khan, the governor of his prison.

For the next three days, till he left Agra, Aurangzeb continued with his charade of being a devoted and dutiful son. He called a special assembly of the Omrah, where he read out a letter he had written to his father, one which he had no intention of sending. 'I am only a guardian of the empire until Your Majesty is restored to full health. I will not, however, desist till I have captured Dara who is the cause of all strife in the empire. Once I have accomplished this task, I will present myself before Your Majesty like an obedient son and you shall be Lord and Master of the Mughal dominions as before.'

In the second week of June, ten days after their arrival in Agra, the news spread that Aurangzeb and Murad had started for Delhi in pursuit of Prince Dara. Their two armies, separated by a short distance of a mile or so, were marching along the banks of the Jamuna, the river's waters reduced to a trickle during the dry summer months. Disguised as a mendicant from Kashmir to explain my blue eyes and fair colouring, I joined their train. This was the only way of catching up with my master and once again dedicating myself to his service. In the rage that continued to consume me, I felt no risk to be too great.

Our first halt was near Mathura. Knowing well the perfidy Aurangzeb was capable of, I could anticipate what was to come when I heard the soldiers discussing the lavish gifts Aurangzeb had been showering on Murad. Not only had the prince sent his brother two hundred and forty Persian horses, forty Ceylon war elephants, twenty-five young and attractive slave girls and two and a half million rupees, but also declared that the time had come for him to fulfil his pledge of crowning Murad the king of Hindustan. He had named an auspicious hour on the fifteenth of June in his dispatches and informed Murad that all preparations for the coronation and the festivities had been made.

Murad's eunuch Shahbaz was suspicious, as before. He entreated his master not to go to Aurangzeb's camp. However, Murad, ever boastful, had laughed at Shahbaz's warnings and replied with his usual, immodest claim, '*Az man kase bahadur nist* (None is braver than I)'.

Aurangzeb and his officers received Murad's party with joyous expressions of welcome. Aurangzeb led Murad to his own seat in the vast blue tent erected specially for the coronation. He stood next to him like a servant, wiping away the sweat from Murad's face with a handkerchief and driving away the flies with a fly-whisk. Musicians and dancers, male and female, appeared. While they performed, rosewater was sprinkled over the guests. The feast began at two in the afternoon and continued for three hours, after which Aurangzeb's officers invited members of Murad's party to their tents for sessions of drinking and amorous sport with dancing girls brought from Delhi and Agra for the purpose. Hearing the sounds of music and mirth from Aurangzeb's camp and concluding that their officers had settled down to a night of festivity, Murad's soldiers, too, relaxed their guard. They wandered out in search of food for themselves and forage for their horses. Murad and the faithful Shahbaz were now the only ones left in Aurangzeb's tent, where the prince was plied with more food and drink.

Aurangzeb left soon after, saying he was off to oversee the preparations for the coronation the next morning, and urged his brother to enjoy what was to come next. Five enchanting dancing girls, the curves and swells of their supple bodies transparent through the folds of finest Dacca muslin, entered the tent, their eyes darting an unmistakable invitation as they began to dance. Murad's one remaining eye—the other had been lost to Ram Singh's spear thrust in the battle—began to shine in lust. He unbuckled his sword, laid aside his dagger, and untied the knot of his *qaba*. Stretching out on the divan, he asked for another cup of the special Persian wine he had liberally imbibed through the afternoon. He then gestured to the most attractive girl in the group to join him. The other girls quietly left the tent. From the entrance, one of them signalled to Shahbaz that he should afford his master privacy. As soon as Shahbaz emerged from the tent, he was lifted off his feet by eight soldiers. They left him no time to call out or use his weapons, but strangled and buried him in an already prepared grave. Inside the tent, Murad had submitted himself to a gentle, soothing massage with fragrant oils. Soon he was snoring. When the girl saw that he was in deep slumber, she put on her clothes, took Murad's weapons and quietly stole out. Six men now entered the tent, and chained Murad's feet in fetters. On the day of his 'coronation', Murad Baksh, the second son of the Great Mogul, was spirited away to the Gwalior prison, where he was later killed. His young son, who had survived the battle of Samugarh in the howdah under the protection of his father's shield, was poisoned before he reached manhood.

This was the first time that I was not agitated by yet more evidence of Aurangzeb's duplicity, but was in fact delighted by its outcome. Murad Baksh had richly deserved his fate.

I had set out for Delhi in the hope of joining the Wali Ahad's fleeing party but was told by the Jesuit fathers, whom I visited on the evening of my arrival, that it was close to two days since they had left. The fathers asked me to stay with them since my own house, abandoned by the servant and the two guards I had left behind, was unsafe in these lawless times.

The fathers had not changed, except that Father Malpica's paunch had shrunk, Father Buze was quieter and stroked his beard more thoughtfully and more often, while Father Roth had become even more cutting than before.

'He could have made common cause with his brother Shuja in Bengal but chose instead to escape westwards to Lahore where he hopes to raise a fresh army,' Father Roth said, expressing doubt about the success of the prince's mission.

Father Buze, still loyal to his friend, remonstrated, 'What else could he have done? After the governor of Delhi behaved so shamefully by refusing to obey the emperor's orders and closing the city's gates and the imperial treasure house to the Wali Ahad!'

'Just as the victorious are inundated with avowals of fealty, betrayals are the lot of the defeated,' the German priest tried to be conciliatory.

'I can only say that the prince's fate has become a hammer and he the anvil,' Father Buze addressed me. 'The armies under Sulaiman Shukoh, on which he had laid such great store to redeem his fortunes, no longer exist. Prince Dara had no option but to flee Delhi.'

'There have been more betrayals,' Father Roth enlightened me on the latest happenings. 'Of Sulaiman's two chief commanders, Diler Khan has switched his loyalty to Aurangzeb. Raja Jai Singh, who had grown to hate the Wali Ahad since the siege of Kandahar when the prince had called him a *mirasi*, has led his Rajputs back to his own dominions of Jaipur. Sulaiman Shukoh is left with no troops except his father's personal guard.'

Reluctantly, I agreed that as the war neared its end, it increasingly appeared that Prince Dara had indeed been singled out by an implacable and malevolent providence.

I was eager to set out for Lahore the very next day, but the fathers restrained me, saying that the troubles in the empire had made the highways unsafe. Since the fear of the emperor's regime had waned, oppressed peasants were pouring out of their wretched villages, robbing and plundering travellers. I should wait, they advised, until a large enough group of armed travellers had assembled to set out for Lahore.

The journey to Lahore was slow since we were careful to travel only during daytime. At noon, we would halt to feed and rest the animals and then travel for another couple of hours till we reached a serai where we could seek shelter in some security. On the highway outside Panipat, fifty miles west of Delhi, we passed a newly erected tower pierced all round by several openings. Placed in each window at intervals of two feet, were several severed heads of robbers who had been caught and executed. A small boy in a tattered loincloth,

no more than three years of age, the tip of his tongue flicking on the
snot plastered between his nose and his upper lip, was staring at one
of the heads. A mangy dog, a large tumour bulging under the skin of
its neck, sat crouched next to the boy, chewing on a bone of uncertain
provenance. It could not have been long since the execution had taken
place. The heads were still not wholly decomposed and gave out a foul
odour. For a brief moment, my eyes tricked my brain and the heads I
saw were those of my friends in Prince Dara's entourage: Wazir Khan,
Rustam Khan, Khwaja Younis. I shook my head violently to rid it of
these ominous imaginings.

The prince's eyes brimmed with tears when I presented myself
at his court in Lahore. The recent events had left their mark on his
face; he looked years older than he had just a few weeks ago when
he had charged at Aurangzeb's army atop Fateh Jang. There were
deep furrows around his eyes that frequently became moist from
uncontrolled emotion; the white hairs in his beard and eyebrows were
visible even from a distance.

'Look!' the prince said turning to his officers, his voice hoarse
with emotion. 'Look at the fidelity of this *farangi* lad! He is neither of
my religion, nor of my race. Nor has he eaten of my salt for long. Yet
he has come to join me, passing through dangers and risking his life.
Those whom I retained in my service for so many years, who gladly
accepted gifts and favours, have abandoned me in my hour of need
with base ingratitude and disloyalty.'

He ordered that a horse be given to me and that it be brought in at
once. The prince personally inspected the horse, and not satisfied with
its look asked for another. He then presented me with five hundred
rupees and ordered that my pay be doubled. I had no difficulty in
finding appropriate lodging in Lahore as several of my European
friends who had served in the prince's artillery, and had escaped from
Agra before Aurangzeb's arrival, were already residing there and kindly
asked me to join them.

With fresh news arriving daily of Aurangzeb's imminent arrival
in Delhi in pursuit of the prince, raising a new army had become a

matter of utmost urgency. Although Prince Dara now had twenty thousand horsemen in his service, they were far from being a fighting force that could resist Aurangzeb's armies. His hopes lay with the Rajput prince Rajrup Singh whose territory in Jammu adjoined the mountainous kingdom of Kashmir. Rajrup Singh, who had served under the Wali Ahad in the siege of Kandahar, had a cavalry of fifteen thousand and an infantry of three hundred thousand Rajputs. He had offered his support on condition that the prince would provide him sufficient funds. The Wali Ahad, who had protected and supported Hindus throughout his life, still laid store in the honour and fidelity of the Rajput kings. He at once gave the raja one million rupees. To bind him further to his cause, he sent the raja to Nadira Begum, who gave Rajrup Singh many presents, addressed him as her son, as dear to her as Sulaiman Shukoh. She then did something that was unprecedented among the Moguls. Since there was no milk in her breasts, she washed them with water and offered the Rajput this water to drink. Rajrup Singh drank the water and solemnly swore he would always be true to her and never fail his duties as a son. Then, promising to return with his army, he left for his kingdom with the money. In the next ten days, as Aurangzeb's army approached, Prince Dara sent Rajrup Singh frantic messages summoning the raja to his aid, but the messages were met with silence. Betrayal, which had been quietly tiptoeing into the prince's fate, had now taken full possession of it.

I witnessed the consternation in the court when the news arrived that the vanguard of Aurangzeb's army under the command of Khalilullah had crossed the river Sutlej at Ropar. The only natural obstacle that now remained between Aurangzeb's forces and Lahore was the river Beas. The prince wavered. At times he was determined to strengthen the fort, summon the nobles of the neighbouring provinces to come to his aid and make a last valiant effort. At other times he gave in to despair. 'There is no hope,' he said to his assembled officers one day. 'It is better that this half-dead man leave the world so he is saved from witnessing the slaughter of his wives and children.'

'The Holy Quran says that hopelessness in a Muslim is as great a sin as infidelity,' the chief commander Daud Khan gently reminded him, seeking to steel the prince's resolve. He suggested the prince stay at Lahore while he proceeded with the bulk of the forces to contest the crossing of the Beas. But the delay on the prince's part in reaching a decision proved costly. Khalilullah had already crossed the Beas. When the prince heard that Aurangzeb himself had reached Ropar with another large army, he decided there was no option left but to flee from Lahore.

I will not describe the hardships we faced as our army of a few thousand horsemen abandoned one fort after another, Aurangzeb's troops under Khalilullah Khan and Raja Jai Singh, who had joined the new emperor, in hot pursuit. It seemed even the saints with whom he had enjoyed such close commerce had abandoned Prince Dara's cause. I felt pity for the prince as he desperately clutched at occult straws and hoped for supernatural interventions to restore his fortunes. In Multan, he asked the descendants of the famous Sufi saint Sheikh Baha-ud-din Zakaria to intercede with the Prophet on his behalf.

'We will certainly do so,' they said. 'We will remain awake during the night so as to be the first ones to receive an audience at dawn with Prophet Mohammed.' In the morning, they appeared with downcast eyes and said that though they had waited in the Prophet's antechamber the entire night they were unable to speak to him—because he had been conversing with Aurangzeb! This continued for three days. Prince Dara still did not waver in his regard for saints, and knaves who pretended to be such. He presented them with twenty-five thousand rupees and a costly chadar of the finest cloth to be spread over the tomb of Baha-ud-din.

From Multan, we headed westwards in long marches, moving day and night, our strength reduced through desertions to five thousand cavalry and five thousand infantry. The guns, ammunition and supplies that would be required to withstand a long siege were loaded in five hundred boats that sailed for the fortress of Bhakkar. When we reached the fortress, which stood on a rocky island in the middle of the Indus where all the five rivers of the Punjab meet, the prince decided that two thousand of his select soldiers would be left behind at Bhakkar to deny the enemy a crossing. The prince himself would make for Gujarat through Sind with the rest of his troops to raise another army. I begged the prince to take me with him.

'I would like to take all of you with me, my faithful *farangi* lad, but this fortress must be held to stop the advance of the traitors. That is the only chance we have to reverse our fortunes.'

I protested. I entreated.

'I promise you, Manucci,' he said gently, 'that when I am emperor you will be an Amir at the court. I now double your salary to three hundred rupees. You shall also be the captain of the Europeans. And to console you for my absence'—a rare smile appeared on his face like the sun emerging from behind dark monsoon clouds—'you shall have a boatload of the best wines from Kabul and Persia.'

This was the last time I saw the prince. The news of a rare success in raising an army of twenty thousand horsemen in Gujarat and his faith that the Rajput princes, Jaswant Singh of Jodhpur and the Maharana of Udaipur, who owed so much to his intercessions on their behalf with Emperor Shah Jahan would come to his aid, gave all of us who had remained behind fleeting hope. But the prince's spiteful fate would only be content with his total ruin. The Rajputs stayed in their dominions and the prince's small army was decimated at Deorai. He was now in headlong flight through the harsh lands of Gujarat and Sind, with his wives and children and a few hundred men. It was only a question of time before Aurangzeb's forces would capture the prince.

As if foreordained, the prince's capture came through a final betrayal. He was taken prisoner by the Afghan Malik Jivan, with whom he had sought shelter in the northernmost reaches of the empire. Jivan was the same man whose life he had saved not once but twice from his father's wrath.

The twenty-ninth of August 1659. The day of the greatest infamy in the history of the Moguls. Bile rises in my mouth as I remember.

A sunny morning, without a cloud to mar the deep blue of the sky, held no foreboding of the dark hours that awaited my beloved prince. Hoarse, throbbing drums led the sorry parade. And then the prince came into sight. His mount was no longer the majestic Fateh Jang, adorned in a gilt harness, his howdah crafted out of gold and silver shaded from the sun by a magnificent velvet canopy, but an undersized, worn-out female elephant liberally caked with mud and destined for slaughter. Deliberately fed on a diet of corn, cabbage and beans the previous evening, the animal's booming farts accompanied the procession like the irregular beats of a discordant drum. Having gorged on decades of hate so that his very spittle turned into bile whenever he thought of Prince Dara, the monster Aurangzeb could not heap enough indignity on a man far his superior in all qualities of head and heart that make a prince immortal in the shared memories of his people. Aurangzeb's attempt to humiliate the Wali Ahad by parading him in the sorriest of plights only lent him an air of tragic nobility. The Wali Ahad and his youngest son Sipir Shukoh, no more than a boy, clad in torn, dirty clothes, were seated in the open howdah, their hands and feet fettered in iron chains and their coarse cotton turbans covered in filth. Those who stood in the front rows of the onlookers and were in a position to observe the expression on the prince's face tell me that it was serene, as if his soul was already viewing realms hidden from human eyes. Nazar Beg, whom I recognized as a slave the prince had often chastised, sat behind them with a raised sword. A squadron of mail-clad cavalry, their naked swords glinting in the sun, rode on both sides of the elephant. Behind them was a sight that made my blood boil: a procession of the vilest traitors that ever lived—Malik Jivan and his Afghans, who had betrayed the prince to the pursuing forces of Raja Jai Singh and Bahadur Khan, rode behind the elephant.

Onlookers wept openly. I could hear shrieks and piercing wails of distress from women crowding the balconies. Indians have tender hearts but little physical courage. Although some women threw ashes and pots filled with urine and faeces on the heads of the traitorous Afghans riding below—which they parried with their shields—not one person made a single move or drew a sword to deliver the prince they loved and admired. I am ashamed to admit that after living for so many years among Indians, my own blood ran tepid in my veins. My sword, too, remained stuck in the scabbard. The impulse to draw it and rush to my beloved prince's assistance remained just that—an impulse.

Informed of the sympathy Prince Dara had aroused among Delhi's inhabitants, Aurangzeb decided on a quick execution. Danishmand Khan was the only Amir who protested the decision and recommended that the prince be confined in the state prison at Gwalior. Circumspect as always, with blood as cold as that of his French retainer, that scoundrel M. Bernier, he took care to couch his opposition in terms of the effect the execution of a royal prince would have on India's image in the courts of Persia and Turkey. He was scrupulous not to utter any words that could be construed as favourable to Prince Dara's person. But the opportunity was too rife for the tyrant to be distracted from it, and he entrusted Nazar Beg with the foul task.

When the rumours surrounding the circumstances of the prince's execution finally settled, the images of the gruesome deed swam in my head. The Afghans had barged into the prince's cell at nightfall just as father and son, who had refused food sent by the jailor for fear of being poisoned, were boiling lentils for their evening meal. They had caught hold of the boy, forcibly separated him from his father and dragged him into the adjoining cell. The piteous shrieks of his son continued to reach the prince till the last moment after he himself had been overpowered, and Nazar Beg had severed his head from his trunk. The ingrate then calmly wiped his sword against the cloth covering the lower part of the prince's body and sent word to Aurangzeb that his order had been carried out.

What I heard afterwards and then witnessed with my own eyes in the days that followed made me feel as though I were sinking in a swamp of black, fetid grief. Aurangzeb, who had been anxiously awaiting the news, ordered that Prince Dara's head be washed of blood and brought to him on a dish. He then stamped on the face and said, 'Take it away from my sight. I did not look at the face of this apostate when he was alive, and I do not wish to do so now.' The prince's head was hung from a peg above the main gate of the palace for three days, rotting in the sun. An unending smoke of flies drifted over it before it was joined to the trunk and the corpse interred, unwashed and unprayed over, in an unmarked grave under the vault in the tomb of their great-great grandfather, Humayun.

After the unspeakable murder of the Wali Ahad, I sank into a melancholic stupor which lasted almost six months. Sitting alone in my garden in the evenings, tears leaking out of the corners of my eyes, I wept at the fate of the prince. My thoughts, each beginning with 'If only . . .' obsessively circled around all that could have happened to allow the Wali Ahad to return victorious from the war and be crowned the emperor. If only the turncoat Jai Singh, a blot on the fair name of Rajputs, had pursued Shuja after his defeat as vigorously as he later pursued Prince Dara in service of Aurangzeb. If only the prince had been less trusting of the traitor Khalilullah Khan. If only . . .

Since I was known to have been partisan to Prince Dara, the Omrah hesitated to call me to their harems in case of sickness. My place was filled by M. Bernier who, on the recommendation of Danishmand Khan, was appointed as one of Aurangzeb's personal physicians. Prince Dara's harem had scattered, its inmates absorbed into the harems of Aurangzeb and his sons. Nadira Begum, who had accompanied her husband on his flight through the harsh desert lands of Sind, had ingested poison after they were captured by the Afghans. Unable to reconcile to her future fate as Aurangzeb's concubine, she preferred to end her life rather than become part of the spoils gracing his triumph. Prince Dara's first love and my first medical disaster, Meher Begum, remained steadfast in rejecting Aurangzeb's invitations to enter his harem. When the new emperor sent word that he was captivated by her hair, Meher Begum cut off her thick tresses and sent them to him with the message, 'Here is the hair you found so attractive.' Aurangzeb persisted. Her beauty was incomparable, he said, and he wanted her as one of his wives. Meher Begum slashed her face with a knife, collected the blood in a cloth and sent it to Aurangzeb with the note that if he sought the beauty of her face, it was now undone, and if her blood gratified him he was welcome to it. Impressed by her steadfastness, Aurangzeb left her alone.

I fervently hoped that he suffered unbearable pangs of jealousy at Prince Dara's ability to evoke such loyalty in a woman even after his death. I was loath to concede that although Aurangzeb was a heartless monster, capable of the most foul acts of murder and perfidy, he had one redeeming quality. Although he shared the Islamic view that regards women less than men, he yet accorded them a higher place in the social order than most Muslims did. 'A woman is not an instrument that can be hung against the wall when you have played on it; she is a man's equal partner in the grand drama of creation,' he is reported to have said. This is the only grey strand I can discern in the otherwise total blackness of Aurangzeb's fiendish soul.

In the worst period of my gloom, I wished I could follow the example of Prince Dara's elephant. They say that after the Wali Ahad's execution, the keeper of the elephant came sobbing to the animal and throwing his arms around its trunk said, 'Unhappy Fateh Jang! What will become of you now that your master is dead?' On hearing this, the elephant began to gather dust from the ground and throw it over its head with its trunk. It then sank to the ground on its knees and refused all food and water. Within a fortnight it was dead.

My misery was no doubt made worse by the complete lack of companionship. Most of my friends from the Wali Ahad's court were either dead or in prison. The rest had left Delhi and were scattered all over the country. The neighbouring house of the Jesuits, where I had spent many convivial evenings, lay empty. The fathers had been expelled from Delhi soon after Aurangzeb's coronation and had returned to their original home in Agra. I myself lived in constant fear of a knock on the door announcing the arrival of a court official ordering me to vacate the house Prince Dara had allotted me.

I was young then, and the dismal apathy began to lift once the resilience of youth joined the fray in earnest. Perhaps it is more accurate to say that my sorrow retreated into the deeper reaches of my heart. The prince and my friends rose from the dead only in my sleep. During the day I was calm, sometimes even cheerful. It was only at dawn that I would awake from an uneasy sleep with my eyelids wet from the tears I had shed in my dreams.

Oddly, it was the day on which I witnessed Sarmad's execution that I felt the stone that had been weighing on my spirit finally lift. Early on a December morning the naked poet, who had spread such joy with his wit and verse in the prince's court, was taken to the square in front of the royal citadel to be executed. Low pale light was just beginning to spread across the land. It promised to be a bright day, but to those gathered at the square its menace was as palpable as a blade of knife. Perhaps it was the courage with which Sarmad faced the executioners that cut through the web in which my soul had been enmeshed for the last few months.

As Sarmad mounted the scaffold, I heard his voice, powerful yet honey-sweet, sing out to the executioner's sword:

'I see the Spirit shine in your steel,
Come and possess this body.
I do not despise you,
I adore the Spirit in your sharp edge.
You are my friend, my saviour,
Come.'

He knelt on the wooden platform and laid his head on the block as though it were a feather-soft pillow that he was settling on for a long sleep. The next moment, I saw his severed head rolling on the ground, the neck spurting blood into the dust.

I decided in that instant to leave the empire that was now ruled by a monster.

For a year now, I have been living in Goa, in my old teacher Vaidraj's village. He is an old man and is insistent that before he leaves this life he wants to teach me all he knows. I am like his son, he says. I accompany him to homes of the sick in other villages where I watch him closely as he practises his healing arts. In the evening, we discuss the patients we have visited during the day and he teaches me the secrets of the medicine the Hindus call Ayurveda, the science of long life.

I often sit in the shade of the banyan tree in the courtyard where I have begun to write an account of my travels. Living among these simple, kind people, sharing the undemanding rhythm of their lives, discovering a guardian I never had, I find myself becoming more tolerant. I have even discovered a hidden vein of pity for my father. I now understand that his violent nature was born out of hopelessness. I can understand his need to drink himself into the only element where he felt at home, brutal oblivion. Sometimes, as I lie alone at night under the banyan tree, drifting in the realm between wakefulness and sleep, images of Mala or Maria come unbidden to my mind. I know that an expedition to the capital city for the purpose of meeting them will be futile. Mala must be old now, not in years but in her soul, for her profession ages a woman as no passage of time ever can. The sultry fragrance of her bosom which I had breathed is lost forever. As for Maria, what will be the point of trying to meet her? Even if she is still in Goa and has not returned to Portugal? She will have children, and a husband she perhaps cherishes. Like many women who have found a new love she would not like to be reminded of one she had abandoned. Embers of old love cannot be blown into a fire. At best, they will only glow for a moment before they scatter ash on the blower.

I know I will soon begin my travels again. My wish is to visit the kingdoms of Bijapur and Golconda and move further south to the newly established British fort of Madras. One day, I will return to Venice. My dream is still intact, though more out of habit and for want of a replacement; its original allure is lost, its colours have become dull. India has entered my blood. I love its myriad, various landscapes and lean cattle. I love this land even as I pity the wretched Hindus, whose religion is being so ruthlessly persecuted by the monstrous being who sits on the throne of Hindustan. A mosque stands at the place of their holiest temple in Benares. Another mosque has been erected on the site of the great temple of Mathura that was of such a height that its gilded pinnacle could be seen from Agra, eighteen leagues away. Hindu festivals have been outlawed. Special taxes, such as the *jazia*, the poll tax on unbelievers, have been imposed on them. The sale of Hindu girls to foreign traders is encouraged, 'to rid the country of the abomination of heathenism,' he says. Hindu children are allowed to be castrated for employment as eunuchs in the palaces of the Omrah. Many Hindu seats of learning, such as the one that was headed by Kavindracharya, have been shut down. The persecution of Sikh gurus has never been as vengeful. Christian and Parsi places of worship have been turned into stables for imperial cavalry. In the meantime, reviled by Hindus and revered by most Muslims of Sunni persuasion, Aurangzeb continues to rule as the undisputed ruler of Hindustan. In the Bible, God says, 'By me the kings reign.' Only He knows why He raises a man to the throne to be either a scourge or a solace to his subjects. Before I left Delhi, I heard a song in its bazaars that demonstrated to me that the inhabitants of the capital were becoming reconciled to the new regime. The song was a lament about the fickleness of fortune, which 'changes a fakir's cowl, while it beheads a prince in passing'. The 'fakir' refers, naturally, to Aurangzeb. I do not remember the remaining lines. The song is still popular in Hindustan although Aurangzeb has forbidden its singing under penalty of the singer losing his tongue.

'If you would be king, never leave a wounded prince alive'

FRANCOIS BERNIER

BACK IN FRANCE AND objectively reflecting on my experiences in the Mogul empire from a distance, unfettered by the inevitable distortions that come from being a participant, I find I have no cause to revise my opinions of Aurangzeb's character. Indeed, my first impressions have now changed into firm convictions.

Aurangzeb, or Alamgir, as he is now named as emperor, is a remarkable sovereign whose policies have remained consistent with the twin pillars of his vision of himself as a monarch: the welfare of the empire and the spread of Islam. The apparent contradictions in his intent and actions resolve themselves if one comprehends the two forces that drove his life's mission.

As an illustration, I shall take the example of his second coronation on the twelfth day of May, 1659, which I was privileged to attend as secretary to Danishmand Khan (who had then been reappointed as foreign minister), an occasion which has been rightly described by court historians as more splendid than any held in the history of

Islam in India. Indeed, it was a spectacle the likes of which I had not witnessed in my ten years of association with the Mogul court.

Seven hundred master decorators worked day and night for two weeks to embellish the pillars, walls and ceiling of the Hall of Public Audience in the grand fort in Delhi with gold and pearls in singular designs and unmatched craftsmanship. The splendour of the coronation parade, too, was beyond any comparison. Twelve brass bands led four contingents of war elephants, a brigade of cavalry and five hundred infantry men clad in brilliantly coloured uniforms. Aurangzeb was seated in a howdah resembling the black marble throne in the fort at Agra. He wore a turban studded with diamonds, rubies and sapphires in alternate rows, which sparked off a new fashion in turbans among the Omrah. The ceremony lasted for three hours and reached its climax when, after taking his seat on the Peacock Throne, the monarch placed a gilded copy of the Quran on his head and pledged to 'live and rule by the directives inscribed in this most sacred of all books in the universe'. A fanfare of trumpets sounded from four corners of the Red Fort and hundreds of pigeons were released from their cages, signifying the beginning of a new era. In the city, people gathered to pray en masse and the poor were fed in droves, and celebratory dance and music performances by professional troupes drawn from all quarters of the empire livened the main squares.

How could this unmatched glamour and pageantry be reconciled with Aurangzeb's professed principle of promoting Islamic simplicity? The people who serve him do not doubt the simplicity, nay, the austerity of his personal life. The monarch darns his own socks, stitches his own clothes, sleeps on a board of unpolished wood, eats the simplest fare and drinks no wine. He would rather walk than be carried in a litter on the shoulders of palanquin bearers. But he knows well that the way to the heart of the people of Hindustan, even or especially the idolaters whose religion he despises, lies in an unending display of public grandeur combined with an ascetic private life. The former, the pomp of power, they expect from his station as a sovereign, whereas the latter is a sign of his humanity they can identify with as their own lot.

The quality that sets Aurangzeb apart from most monarchs and one he shares with a few other rulers in history—I speak here of the Roman emperor Julius Caesar, Henry VII of England, Shah Abbas of Persia—is his single-mindedness in the pursuit of his goals that does not leave the slightest room for sentiment in his means of achieving them. No confusion has ever waited on his banners. He is strong because his will is implacable and his actions are dictated purely by reasons of state, recognizing no ties of love, affection or loyalty. He imprisoned his father, the erstwhile emperor, in the fort at Agra where the latter died under mysterious circumstances after twelve years of captivity, not because Aurangzeb wished to avenge the favours his father had showered on Dara while neglecting him, but because he recognized the potential threat posed by the scheming old man to his reign in Hindustan. He knew well the machinations that were at play, whether it was of his father's command to his guard of three thousand Tartar women to capture the prince when he entered the fort after his victory at Samugarh, or the old emperor's attempt to win over his jailer, Sultan Muhammad, Aurangzeb's son, and the similar overtures made by him to Murad.

Murad, whom Aurangzeb seized immediately after their triumph over the imperial forces led by Prince Dara and later ordered to be killed by *post*, his preferred slow-acting poison, could not be left alive to claim the throne he believed had been promised to him by his brother. It is a harsh but essential requirement for securing peace and stability in an empire that all competitors for the throne must be expeditiously eliminated. 'If you would be king, never leave a wounded prince alive,' seemed to be the principle ruling his actions, a principle that was not only personal but enshrined in the annals of the dynasty. This imperative also applied to Prince Dara's son Sulaiman Shukoh, who was captured after defeat in battle. Many have maligned the emperor for refusing to grant Sulaiman's wish to be executed immediately and for prolonging his suffering by the administration of repeated doses of *post*, but the emperor's actions were driven by the assertion that his nephew had to be kept alive for a few months to reveal the existence of other devious plots that could have been afoot.

Some have expressed shock that Aurangzeb had his eldest son, Sultan Muhammad, poisoned, as also his sister Roshanara Begum, both of whom had rendered him invaluable support during the events leading to the war of succession. The executions, for I refuse to call them murders, were necessary for the two reasons I have stated above. Sultan Muhammad had begun to boast that it was to him that Aurangzeb should feel indebted for his crown, a precursor to the belief that it was he rather than his father who deserved to wear it. By a fortuitous coincidence, after he had sent Sultan Muhammad to the state prison in Gwalior, I was summoned by the emperor for a consultation on his insomnia that had again taken hold of his nights, and was witness to Aurangzeb advising his second son, Sultan Muazzam, who stood before him with his head bowed and his shoulders sagging in a posture of utter submission: 'Be wise, or a fate similar to that which has befallen your brother awaits you. Do not indulge in the fatal delusion that Aurangzeb may be treated by his children as was his grandfather by his son Shah Jahan, or that, like the latter, he will permit the sceptre to fall from his hands.'

Roshanara Begum, too, believing that her brother's ascension to the throne gave her license to indulge in sexual excesses that became the scandal of Delhi, did not realize that her brother neither acknowledged any debts of gratitude nor expected any thankfulness for favours he granted. When the emperor discovered that his sister kept eight young men in her palace for her pleasure—this was after he had announced the appointment of a Protector of Public Morals in all cities with a population of more than ten thousand to enforce bans on gambling, drinking and prostitution and the playing of music and had introduced the Sharia punishment of stoning to death a woman caught indulging in illicit carnal relations—he did her a favour by poisoning her and thus sparing her the ignomity of a public lynching.

The only occasion when the emperor's feelings overcame his reason was in his treatment of Prince Dara after the latter's capture by the imperial forces led by Raja Jai Singh and Bahadur Khan. All those who had the greatest admiration for the emperor's ability to remain calm under grave provocation, were shocked by the intensity of his hatred, which came pouring out like sulphurous lava. But does this outburst of emotion not belie the accusation that he was cold and often appeared devoid of all human emotion? I can personally vouch for the falsity of the canard that he ordered the severed head of Dara to be wrapped as a gift parcel and sent to their father imprisoned in the Agra fort and that the old emperor, at first overjoyed that his son was finally rediscovering a filial sentiment, swooned when he opened the parcel and beheld its gory contents. It is true that the inhabitants of Delhi, chiefly the idolaters and Mohammedans of a lower order, almost rose in revolt at Aurangzeb's treatment of his elder brother when he was brought to Delhi as a prisoner. I must point out, however, that such gratuitous cruelty is not the province of an individual but a general feature of the oriental character. I am convinced that after this particular episode of loss of control, the monarch's rare displays of rage in public were just calculated shows designed to intimidate rather than spontaneous outbursts.

For Aurangzeb, the spread of Islam and guarding it from contamination by infidels, as also the undermining of Quranic precepts by liberal interpretations of heretics within its own fold, were higher missions than securing the Mogul empire; one can say that the latter was a necessary precondition for the former. The harsh steps he took to weaken, if not destroy, the religion of the idolaters had been constrained by the necessity of preserving the empire which, in turn, made these steps possible. Indeed, he has been freer in stamping out heresy within Islam, executing many Shia, Bohra and Sufi saints who were unwilling to follow the orthodox Sunni faith. No one can doubt that a personal commitment to a religion, which we in Europe rightly regard as theologically naïve and morally primitive, is the guiding force of his life. His first act after the coronation, the prohibition of stamping on coins the *kalimah*, 'La 'ilaha illallah mohammedur-rasulallah (There is no God but Allah, Mohammed is Allah's messenger)'—lest the words of

God become polluted by the touch of unworthy hands, is proof of the omnipresence of Islam in his life and its status as the prime mover of his actions. No one who knows India and has observed the emperor from close quarters can doubt that he has immeasurably strengthened the roots of both the empire and Islam and that for centuries to come European nations will have to take both these facts into account in their commerce with that land.

Epilogue

'I AM CONTENT, TRULY,' I say to Khwaja Chisti, responding more to the pity in his voice than his expressed regret that all he can offer his old friend is a lowly position in Danishmand Khan's household. 'That I will serve out the rest of my days here, and will never be a Nazir in the emperor's harem, is not even a minor misfortune in the larger scheme of things. Emperor Shah Jahan—ruler of universe—spent the last twelve years of his life as a prisoner in a palace he had built for his pleasure, but which the wheel of destiny sought fit to turn into his gaol. No, my friend, in these dark days it would be blasphemy to complain about my lot.'

We are sitting in the pavilion in Danishmand Khan's garden. Chisti's Agha is away, accompanying Emperor Alamgir on an expedition to Kashmir.

Dusk is approaching. A roseate light, darkening in hue from one moment to the next, spreads above us. For a brief instant I am disoriented as the sky takes on a colour I have seen only at the break of dawn, but the illusion soon vanishes. As the sun dips below the horizon, Chisti says, 'Niamat, the sun has set.'

Chisti is an old friend, but sometimes his penchant for stating the obvious makes me want to tear my hair out.

Author's Note

IT IS IMPORTANT TO note that for all their differences in origin, upbringing and temperament, Francois Bernier and Niccolao Manucci were Europeans of their place and era who viewed Mughal India and Shah Jahan's court through the lens of a sensibility crafted by European prejudices, preoccupations and concerns of the time. Thus, for instance, the attention they devote to Hindu–Muslim and Sunni–Shia differences may well be due to a sharpened European vision for sectarian rifts. As my friend Professor Muzaffar Alam of the University of Chicago, a recognized authority on Mughal India, remarks, this particular sensibility was the heritage of a European polity that had not only purged itself of Jews and Muslims, who had long inhabited their lands, but even of Protestants or Catholics, depending on the religious orientation of the king of the realm. Mughal tolerance for the ways of infidels, at least pre Aurangzeb, was certainly greater than what we encounter in these travellers' accounts. Even in the case of a 'celebrated' bigot like Aurangzeb, of his seven chief ministers four were Shia.

Written from the perspectives of two seventeenth-century European travellers, the novel may not do the Mughals complete justice. This, however, is the fate, and the fascination, of historical fiction, which seeks to give imaginative life to historical events and must find a balance between the emotional truth of its characters and the often ambiguous evidence of history, between the needs of fiction and the demands of historiography. Actually, the liberties I have taken with historical facts are minimal: Danishmand Khan, an exalted noble in Shah Jahan's court, a Mir Bakshi in-charge of giving rank to the nobles and checking their contingents, was a valued adviser on foreign affairs but not the foreign minister; the authorship of *Dabistan-i-Mazahib* is generally attributed to Mobad rather than Dara's drinking companion, Halim.

As always, I would like to acknowledge the inputs of my wife Katha, who is the first—and sometimes the only—reader of my texts before they go to the publishers. The manuscript of this novel, however, had other readers, too: Ravi Singh, who has been editing my work in Penguin for a long time now and has not lost any of his initial zest; Kala Ramesh, who commented on the first draft of the novel; the historians Muzaffar Alam and Farhat Hasan, who were kind enough to point out errors of fact. I am grateful to all of them for their inputs. I also wish to thank Dr Manasi Kumar for her help in procuring library materials related to the period and main characters of this novel and for constantly asking when I was going to finish writing the novel. My gratitude to Poulomi Chatterjee, editor *extraordinaire*, who adopted this fictional child as her own. Her involvement in and contributions to the book are so vital that no expression of thanks can ever be enough.

Select Bibliography

Francoise Bernier, *Travels in the Mogul Empire*, AD 1656–1668, translated by A. Constable, Delhi, 1999

Niccolao Manucci, *Storia do Mogor*, 4 vols., translated by W. Irvine, Delhi, 1989

J.B. Tavernier, *Travels in India*, 2 vols., translated by V. Ball, Madras, 2001

K.R. Qanungo, *Dara Shukoh*, Vol. 1 (second edition), Calcutta, 1952

B. Hasrat, *Dara Shikuh: Life and Works*, Delhi, 1982

T. Hussain, 'The Spiritual Journey of Dara Shukoh', *Social Scientist* 30:78, 2002

Dara Skihoh, *Majma al-Bahrain*, edited and translated by M.M. Haq, Calcutta, 1929

R. Chaudhri, *Dara Shikuh's 'Samudra-Sangama'*, Calcutta, 1954

J. Sarkar, *History of Aurangzeb*, 5 vols., Calcutta, 1912–24

J. Sarkar, *Anecdotes of Aurangzeb*, Delhi, 1988

A. Butenschon, *The Life of a Mughal Princess: Jahan Ara*, London, 1931

K.S. Lal, *The Mughal Harem*, New Delhi, 1988

R. Lal, *Domesticity and Power in the Early Mughal World*, New York, 2005

A. Eraly, *The Last Spring: The Lives and Times of the Great Mughals*, Delhi, 1997

J. Richards, *The Mughal Empire*, Cambridge, 1993

S.A.A. Rizvi, *Muslim Revivalist Movements in Northern India in the Sixteenth and Seventeenth Centuries*, Delhi, 1965

G. Michel, *Mughal Style: The Art and Architecture of Mughal India*, Mumbai, 2007

P.N. Chopra, *Some Aspects of Social Life during the Mughal Age*, Jaipur, 1963

ALSO BY SUDHIR KAKAR

Fiction
Ecstasy
The Ascetic of Desire
Indian Love Stories (Ed.)
Mira and the Mahatma

Non-fiction
Mad and Divine: Spirit and Psyche in the Modern World
Kamasutra: A New Translation (with Wendy Doniger)
The Essential Writings of Sudhir Kakar
Culture and Psyche
The Analyst and the Mystic
The Colors of Violence: Religious–Cultural Identities and Conflict
Intimate Relations: Exploring Indian Sexuality
Tales of Love, Sex and Danger (with J. Ross)
Shamans, Mystics and Doctors: A Psychological Inquiry into India and Its Healing Traditions
Identity and Adulthood (Ed.)
The Inner World: A Psychoanalytic Study of Childhood and Society in India
Conflict and Choice: Indian Youth in a Changing Society (with K. Chowdhry)
Frederick Taylor: A Study in Personality and Innovation